Solve It!

Problem-Solving Strategies

Principal Authors
Michelle Pauls
Dave Youngs

Contributing Author
Myrna Mitchell

Editors
Michelle Pauls
Betty Cordel

Illustrators
Dawn DonDiego
Brock Heasley
Ben Hernandez
Reneé Mason
Margo Pocock
Dave Schlotterback
Brenda Wood

Desktop Publisher
Roxanne Williams

Education Foundation

This book contains materials developed by the AIMS Education Foundation. **AIMS** (**A**ctivities **I**ntegrating **M**athematics and **S**cience) began in 1981 with a grant from the National Science Foundation. The non-profit AIMS Education Foundation publishes hands-on instructional materials (books and the quarterly magazine) that integrate curricular disciplines such as mathematics, science, language arts, and social studies. The Foundation sponsors a national program of professional development through which educators may gain both an understanding of the AIMS philosophy and expertise in teaching by integrated, hands-on methods.

ISBN: **978-1-932093-38-4**

Printed in the United States of America

I Hear and I Forget,

I See and I Remember,

I Do and

I Understand.

-Chinese Proverb

Solve It! 5th.

Problem-Solving Strategies

Introduction

Solve It! 5th: Problem-Solving Strategies is a collection of activities designed to introduce students to nine problem-solving strategies. The tasks included will engage students in active hands-on investigations that allow them to apply their number, computation, geometry, data organization, and algebra skills in problem-solving settings.

It can be difficult for teachers to shift from teaching math facts and procedures to teaching with an emphasis on mathematical processes and thinking skills. One might ask why problem solving should be taught at all. The most obvious reason is that it is part of most mathematics curricula. However, it is also an interesting and enjoyable way to learn mathematics; it encourages collaborative learning, and it is a great way for students to practice the application of mathematical skills. This in turn leads to better conceptual understanding—an understanding that allows students to remember and to apply these skills in different contexts.

Introducing students to the nine strategies included in this book gives them a toolbox of problem-solving methods from which they can draw when approaching problems. Different students might approach the same problem in a variety of ways, some more sophisticated than others. Hopefully, every child can find an approach that he or she can use to solve the problems. Over time, and from discussing what other children have done, students will develop and extend the range of strategies at their disposal.

It is our hope that you will use the problems in this book to enrich your classroom environment by allowing your students to truly experience problem solving. This means resisting the urge to give answers; allowing your students to struggle, and even be frustrated; focusing on the process rather than the product; and providing multiple, repeated opportunities to practice different strategies. Doing this can develop a classroom full of confident problem solvers well equipped to solve problems, both in and out of mathematics, for years to come.

Problem-Solving Strategies

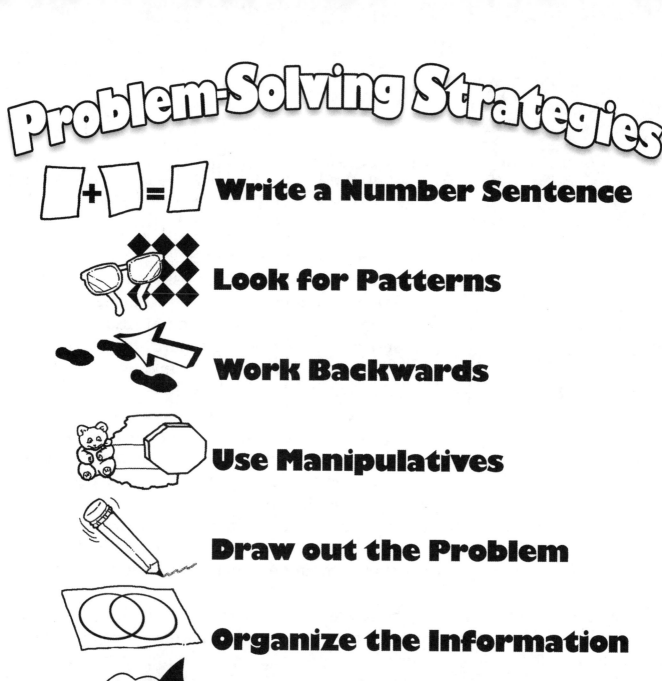

$\square + \square = \square$ **Write a Number Sentence**

Look for Patterns

Work Backwards

Use Manipulatives

Draw out the Problem

Organize the Information

Guess and Check

Use Logical Thinking

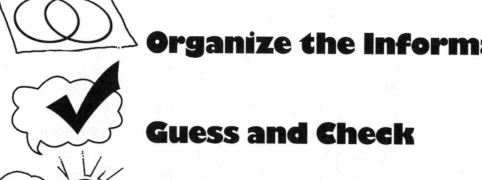

2+2 **Wish for an Easier Problem**

Activities / **Strategies**

Activities	Write a Number Sentence	Look for Patterns	Work Backwards	Use Manipulatives	Draw out the Problem	Organize the Information	Guess and Check	Use Logical Thinking	Wish for an Easier Problem
Fiddling With Fours	X						X		
Gifts Galore	X					X			
Calculating Cake Costs	X			X		X			
Labor Day Dilemma		X				X			
Rules of Arrangement		X		X					
Perpetual Patterns		X		X			X		
Counting the Miles			X			X	X		
Cover-Ups	X		X	X			X		
Credit My Account			X				X		
Cryptically Challenged			X				X	X	
Domino Dilemmas				X				X	
'Picks, Polygons, & Perimeters		X		X		X			
Pondering Partitions				X		X			
Double Play					X	X		X	
Gag Gifts Galore					X	X			
Santa's Ladder					X				
Square Sections		X		X		X			
Counting Quadrilaterals		X				X			
Dueling Dice				X		X		X	
Making Change		X				X	X		
Sam's Sweet Shop				X		X	X		
Circles, Squares, and Sums				X			X		
Three-Digit Divisibility Dilemma		X				X	X		
Square Grid Logic				X				X	
The Missing Piece				X			X	X	
Zoo's Clues						X		X	
How Thick is It?									X
Cut and Stack		X							X
Rages Over Pages						X			X

Problem-Solving Strategies
□ + □ = □ Write a Number Sentence

Sometimes it helps to write down the parts of a problem as a number sentence. Then you can see if what you are doing makes sense. Are you using the right numbers? Are you adding where you should be subtracting? If you have a number sentence, you can answer these questions.

FIDDLING WITH FOURS

Topic
Problem solving

Key Question
How can you combine four fours with mathematical symbols so that the resulting number sentences produce the numbers one through 10?

Learning Goal
Students will practice their computation and problem-solving skills by putting four fours together with mathematical symbols to make number sentences, each producing the numbers from one to 10.

Guiding Documents
Project 2061 Benchmarks
- *Add, subtract, multiply, and divide whole numbers mentally and on paper.*
- *The operations + and - are inverses of each other— one undoes what the other does; likewise x and ÷.*

NCTM Standards 2000*
- *Identify and use relationships between operations, such as division as the inverse of multiplication, to solve problems*
- *Develop fluency in adding, subtracting, multiplying, and dividing whole numbers*
- *Understand and use properties of operations such as the distributive property of multiplication over addition*
- *Build new mathematical knowledge through problem solving*

Math
Whole number operations
Problem solving
Order of operations

Integrated Processes
Observing
Relating
Generalizing

Problem-Solving Strategies
Write a number sentence
Guess and check

Materials
Student pages
Bulletin board space, optional

Background Information
Fiddling With Fours allows students to practice mathematical skills in a problem-solving setting as they are challenged to put four fours together with mathematical symbols to make number sentences, each producing a number from one to 10. The fours can be grouped together (e.g., 444 or 44) or used separately, but each number sentence should use exactly four. The symbols used need not be limited to the basic operations and might include things such as radicals, powers, and factorials. In addition to helping students practice basic computation and problem-solving skills, this activity is a good exercise in order of operations. The extensions your students think of can take the original problem in many different directions and produce a rich mathematical environment in your classroom.

Management
1. When students are introduced to this activity, they may make assumptions about the problem that will prevent them from discovering some of the solutions. Because of this, a thorough explanation, of all the rules is necessary. Students should be aware that they can group fours together (44, 444) in addition to having them separate, and that they can use any mathematical operation, not just the basic four (addition, subtraction, multiplication and division). If students use powers, they should know that the powers do not have to be fours (4^0, 4^1, 4^2, etc.). Also, if the number used in the power is a four, it does not count in the total number of fours used.
2. The nature of this activity makes a proper understanding of order of operations crucial to discovering correct solutions for each number from one to 10. If your students are not completely comfortable with order of operations, a short review is recommended before they begin this activity.
3. This activity is unique in that it asks students to think of their own extensions and explore them as a part of the main problem. This allows students to explore ideas that appeal to them personally and can help make the problem more meaningful. You may wish to devote a portion of a bulletin board or some similar space to the solutions of the original problem as well as the solutions of the various extensions that students explore. This kind of space for the various solutions allows each student to make an individual contribution to a class project. Having a bulletin board for solutions also

gives students the freedom to continue to work on the problem in their spare time and post new solutions as they are discovered.

Procedure

1. Hand out the first student page and go over the instructions. *Combine any four fours with mathematical symbols so that the resulting number sentences produce the numbers one through 10.* Be sure to clarify all of the possibilities such as grouping the fours together, and using operations other than addition, subtraction, multiplication, and division.
2. Have students work in small groups to find as many solutions as they can for each of the numbers from one to 10.
3. When each group has found at least one solution for each number, hand out the second student page and have students answer the questions and pursue an extension that they think of.
4. Close with a time of class discussion where students share the different ways they discovered to write each of the numbers from one to 10 as well as the extensions they pursued.

Connecting Learning

1. How were you able to write each of the numbers from one to 10? (See *Solutions.*)
2. What strategies did you use while working on this problem?
3. Do you notice any interesting things about the solutions you came up with?
4. Were any numbers easier for you to get than others? Why do you think this is?
5. What extensions did you think of to explore?
6. What were the results?

Extensions

These extensions are only a few of the many possible ways to further explore this problem. Hopefully your students will think of these and more and explore them on their own.

1. Create equations for the numbers from 11 to 20 using the same rules.
2. Put no limit on the number of fours that can be used in a given equation.
3. Use combinations of some other number, such as three or five.
4. Only use addition, subtraction, multiplication and division and see if you can still get all of the numbers from one to 10.

Solutions

There are many ways to write each of the numbers from one to 10 using only four fours. A few examples for each number are given below.

One
$(4 + 4) \div (4 + 4)$
$(4 \times 4) \div (4 \times 4)$
$44 \div 44$
$(4 + 4 - 4) \div 4$

Two
$(4 \div 4) + (4 \div 4)$
$(4 \times 4) \div (4 + 4)$
$[4 - (4^0 + 4^0)] \div 4^0$
$[4^2 - (4 + 4)] \div 4$

Three
$(4 + 4 + 4) \div 4$
$(4 \times 4 - 4) \div 4$
$4 - (4 \times 4 \div 4^2)$

Four
$[4 \times (4 - 4)] + 4$
$[4^2 - (4 \times 4)] + 4$
$4^0 + 4^0 + 4^0 + 4^0$
$4^2 - 4 - 4 - 4$

Five
$[(4 \times 4) + 4] \div 4$
$4^2 \div (4 \times 4) + 4$
$(4^3 - 44) \div 4$

Six
$[(4 + 4) \div 4] + 4$
$(4^2 + 4 + 4) \div 4$
$[4 - (4^0 + 4^0)] + 4$
$[4^2 \div (4 + 4)] + 4$

Seven
$4 - (4 \div 4) + 4$
$(44 \div 4) - 4$
$4 + 4^0 + 4^0 + 4^0$
$(44 - 4^2) \div 4$

Eight
$4 + 4 + 4 - 4$
$(4 \times 4) - (4 + 4)$
$4^3 \div [4^2 - (4 + 4)]$
$[4^2 + (4 \times 4)] \div 4$

Nine
$4 \div 4 + 4 + 4$
$(4^2 + 4^2 + 4) \div 4$
$4^2 - (4 + 4 - 4^0)$
$(4^2 + 4) \div 4 + 4$

Ten
$(44 - 4) \div 4$
$4 + 4^0 + 4 + 4^0$
$4^2 - (4 + 4^0 + 4^0)$

* Reprinted with permission from *Principles and Standards for School Mathematics*, 2000 by the National Council of Teachers of Mathematics. All rights reserved.

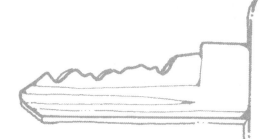

FIDDLING WITH FOURS

Key Question

How can you combine four fours with mathematical symbols so that the resulting number sentences produce the numbers one through 10?

Learning Goal

Students will:

practice their computation and problem-solving skills by putting four fours together with mathematical symbols to make number sentences, each producing the numbers from one to 10.

FIDDLING WITH FOURS

Combine four fours (4s) with mathematical symbols so that the resulting number sentences produce the numbers one through 10. For example, $(4 + 4) \div (4 + 4) = 1$. See if you can find a different way to get one. Next, try to find solutions for each of the numbers from two through 10. There are many different ways to get each number. Do not be limited to addition, subtraction, multiplication, and division. Use the space below to show your solutions.

FIDDLING WITH FOURS

When you have found as many solutions as you can, answer the questions below.

1. Describe the strategies you used while working on this problem.

2. Was it easier for you to come up with solutions for certain numbers? Which ones? Why do you think this is?

3. What extensions can you think of for this activity? List them below.

4. Select the extension that interests you most and explore it. Report your results below.

FIDDLING WITH FOURS

Connecting Learning

1. How were you able to write each of the numbers from one to 10?

2. What strategies did you use while working on this problem?

3. Do you notice any interesting things about the solutions you came up with?

4. Were any numbers easier for you to get than others? Why do you think this is?

5. What extensions did you think of to explore?

6. What were the results?

Gifts Galore

Topic
Problem solving

Key Question
How many gifts are given to the singer of *The Twelve Days of Christmas*, and how much would they cost?

Learning Goals
Students will:
1. determine the total number of gifts described in the song *The Twelve Days of Christmas*, and
2. find the total cost of the gifts.

Guiding Documents
Project 2061 Benchmark
- *Add, subtract, multiply, and divide whole numbers mentally, on paper, and with a calculator.*

NCTM Standards 2000*
- *Develop fluency in adding, subtracting, multiplying, and dividing whole numbers*
- *Build new mathematical knowledge through problem solving*
- *Solve problems that arise in mathematics and in other contexts*
- *Apply and adapt a variety of appropriate strategies to solve problems*
- *Monitor and reflect on the process of mathematical problem solving*

Math
Number and operations
Problem solving

Integrated Processes
Observing
Collecting and recording data
Analyzing

Problem-Solving Strategies
Write a number sentence
Organize the information

Materials
Student pages
Internet access, optional

Background Information
This activity is based on the traditional English song *The Twelve Days of Christmas*. According to *The New Oxford Book of Carols*, this song has its origin in a traditional forfeits game that was played on Twelfth Night, the eve of Epiphany. In games of this type, each player would have to recall the objects recited by previous players and then add one more. While games like this were played in many cultures, *The Twelve Days of Christmas* is probably of Gallic origin.

Some other interesting items about the song are noted in *The New Oxford Book of Carols*. The cally- or colly-birds in the song are blackbirds. The gold rings, which seem out of place in the list, are most likely a corruption of goldspinks, which is the Scottish-dialect term for goldfinches. Originally, then, the gifts for the first seven days were all birds.

In this activity, students are asked to do two things. First, they must find the total number of gifts. To do this, they need to assume that for each day, the gifts given on the previous day are given again. For example, the gifts for the third day include not only the three French hens, but also two more turtle doves and another partridge in a pear tree. Once this is accomplished, students find the total cost of the gifts, using either arbitrary costs or the current market prices for the items.

Management
1. The part of the activity in which students are challenged to determine the costs of the gifts is very open-ended. You can assign an arbitrary cost to each gift; for example, $1 for a partridge in a pear tree, $2 for a turtle dove, $3 for a French hen, and so on. You can also challenge students to research actual prices.
2. If you choose to have students research realistic prices, you will need to provide Internet access and/or appropriate research materials in which they can locate the information. (See *Internet Connections*.)

Procedure
1. Have students get into groups and distribute the student pages.
2. Tell students that they will first find the total number of gifts and then determine the cost of those gifts.

3. When groups have determined the total number, have them share their answers as well as the methods they used to arrive at those answers.
4. Tell the class how you would like them to determine the costs of the gifts (see *Management 1*) and provided the necessary time and materials.
5. Compare results and have students once again share the methods they used to determine their solutions.

Connecting Learning

1. How many gifts are given on the third day? [6] What is the total number of gifts given by the end of the third day? [10]
2. How many gifts are given on the ninth day? [45] What is the total number of gifts given by the end of the ninth day? [165]
3. What is the total number of gifts given? [364]
4. Of which gift(s) is there the most after 12 days? [There are 42 geese and 42 swans.]
5. How many gold rings are there after 12 days? [40] ...French hens? [30] ...swans? [42]
6. Do you notice any patterns in these numbers?
7. What strategies did you use to come up with your answers?
8. How much would the gifts cost?
9. What strategies did you use to come up with this amount?

Solutions

New Gifts Given Each Day
Day One: 1
Day Two: 3
Day Three: 6
Day Four: 10
Day Five: 15
Day Six: 21
Day Seven: 28
Day Eight: 36
Day Nine: 45
Day Ten: 55
Day Eleven: 66
Day Twelve: 78

Total Number of Gifts Each Day
Day One: 1
Day Two: 4
Day Three: 10
Day Four: 20
Day Five: 35
Day Six: 56
Day Seven: 84
Day Eight: 120
Day Nine: 165
Day Ten: 220
Day Eleven: 286
Day Twelve: 364

Total Numbers of Each Gift Given
12 days x 1 partridge in a pear tree = 12 partridges in pear trees
11 days x 2 turtle doves = 22 turtle doves
10 days x 3 French hens = 30 French hens
9 days x 4 calling birds = 36 colly-birds
8 days x 5 gold rings = 40 gold rings
7 days x 6 geese = 42 geese
6 days x 7 swans = 42 swans
5 days x 8 milk maids = 40 milk maids
4 days x 9 drummers = 36 drummers
3 days x 10 pipers = 30 pipers
2 days x 11 dancers = 22 dancers
1 day x 12 lords = 12 lords

Internet Connections

PNC Christmas Price Index
http://www.pncchristmaspriceindex.com
Every year since 1984, PNC Advisors has compiled the "Christmas Price Index," which identifies the cost of purchasing the items in the song *The Twelve Days of Christmas*. The website has graphs showing historical price trends, a short video presentation with all of the information from the most recent Christmas, and interactive games.

* Reprinted with permission from *Principles and Standards for School Mathematics*, 2000 by the National Council of Teachers of Mathematics. All rights reserved.

Gifts Galore

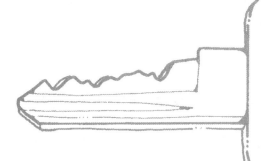

Key Question

How many gifts are given to the singer of *The Twelve Days of Christmas*, and how much would they cost?

Learning Goals

Students will:

1. determine the total number of gifts described in the song *The Twelve Days of Christmas*, and
2. find the total cost of the gifts.

10

Gifts Galore

The Twelve Days of Christmas

On the first day of Christmas my true love sent to me a partridge in a pear tree. On the second day of Christmas my true love sent to me two turtle doves and a partridge in a pear tree. On the third day of Christmas my true love sent to me three French hens, two turtle doves, and a partridge in a pear tree. On the fourth day of Christmas my true love sent to me four colly-birds, three French hens, two turtle doves, and a partridge in a pear tree. On the fifth day of Christmas my true love sent to me five gold rings, four colly-birds, three French hens, two turtle doves, and a partridge in a pear tree.

On the sixth day of Christmas my true love sent to me six geese a-laying…

On the seventh day of Christmas my true love sent to me seven swans a-swimming…

On the eighth day of Christmas my true love sent to me eight maids a-milking…

On the ninth day of Christmas my true love sent to me nine drummers drumming…

On the tenth day of Christmas my true love sent to me ten pipers piping…

On the eleventh day of Christmas my true love sent to me eleven ladies dancing…

On the twelfth day of Christmas my true love sent to me twelve lords-a-leaping, eleven ladies dancing, ten pipers piping, nine drummers drumming, eight maids a-milking, seven swans a-swimming, six geese a-laying, five gold rings, four colly-birds, three French hens, two turtle doves, and a partridge in a pear tree.

Gifts Galore

Study *The Twelve Days of Christmas.* What is the total number of gifts given? What would these gifts cost?

Use the space below to show your work.

Gifts Galore

Connecting Learning

1. How many gifts are given on the third day? What is the total number of gifts given by the end of the third day?

2. How many gifts are given on the ninth day? What is the total number of gifts given by the end of the ninth day?

3. What is the total number of gifts given?

4. Of which gift(s) is there the most after 12 days?

5. How many gold rings are there after 12 days? ...French hens? ...swans?

6. Do you notice any patterns in these numbers?

7. What strategies did you use to come up with your answers?

8. How much would the gifts cost?

9. What strategies did you use to come up with this amount?

CALCULATING CAKE COSTS

Topic
Area:perimeter relationship

Key Question
Why are the "money-saving specials" not actually good deals?

Learning Goals
Students will:
1. evaluate the costs of cakes based on the amount of cake you get for your money,
2. determine why special "money-saving" deals are not actually deals, and
3. compare two cakes to determine which gives you the most for your money.

Guiding Document
NCTM Standards 2000*
- *Use geometric models to solve problems in other areas of mathematics, such as number and measurement*
- *Recognize geometric ideas and relationships and apply them to other disciplines and to problems that arise in the classroom or in everyday life*
- *Explore what happens to measurements of a two-dimensional shape such as its perimeter and area when the shape is changed in some way*
- *Build new mathematical knowledge through problem solving*
- *Solve problems that arise in mathematics and in other contexts*

Math
Geometry
    area:perimeter relationship
Problem solving

Integrated Processes
Observing
Comparing and contrasting
Recording
Interpreting
Analyzing

Problem-Solving Strategies
Write a number sentence
Use manipulatives
Organize the information

Materials
Scissors
Student pages

Background Information
The area of an object as it relates to perimeter is a mathematical concept with many practical applications in the real world. This activity explores the area:perimeter relationship in a very concrete way—cake sizes. In the first part of the activity, students are given the prices for cakes at *Christina's Cake Creations* along with the information that each cake is a perfect square. They are then asked to explain why each of six "money-saving specials" is not worth spending money on. In the second part of the activity, students have to determine which of two options gives the most cake for the price.

What students should quickly realize is that the difference from one cake size to the next is quite significant in terms of the amount of cake you get for your money. While the length of each side only increases by six inches from one cake size to the next, the amount of cake quadruples between a basic and a large, more than doubles between a large and a family, and almost doubles between a family and a party. As this becomes apparent to students, they will be able to clearly explain why each of the specials does not actually give you the most cake for your money.

Management
1. There are two versions of the first page of this activity—an open-ended version and a structured version. Select the page that is most appropriate for your students.
2. Students should work together in small groups on this activity, fostering collaboration and effective mathematical communication.
3. Copy the page of cakes onto card stock and give one copy to each group to cut out. Having a physical manipulative that represents the cakes will help students as they try to expose the flaws in the money-saving specials.

Procedure
1. Distribute the appropriate student page for the first part of the activity to each student. Give students the page of cakes to cut out.
2. Explain the challenge and allow students to get into groups and work on the problem.
3. When groups have had time to explore the problem and develop explanations, have them share why the "deals" are not worth spending money on.
4. Distribute the final student page. If desired, this page can be done individually as an assessment.
5. Close with a final time of class discussion and sharing.

Connecting Learning

1. What flaws are there in Christina's specials? (See *Solutions*.)
2. Which cake gives you the most for your money at the regular prices? [the party cake] Why? [It has an area of 576 in². At $20, that's about $0.03 per square inch.]
3. Which cake gives you the least for your money at the regular prices? [the basic cake] Why? [It has an area of 36 in². At $5, that's about $0.14 per square inch.]
4. As the side lengths of a cake double, what happens to the area? [it quadruples]
5. How many basic cakes would you have to buy to get the same amount of cake as a large? [four] How much more would it cost you? [$10 more]
6. How many large and basic cakes would you have to buy to get the same amount of cake as a family? [two larges, one basic] How much more would it cost you? [$10 more]

Extensions

1. Come up with new prices for the specials that would reflect an actual savings.
2. Have students compare the cake sizes using fractions. For example, one family cake is equal to 2 ¼ large cakes. A party cake is equal to 1 $7/9$ family cakes.
3. Challenge students to develop their own lists of cake sizes and prices. They can then create some "specials" based on the principles they learned in this activity.
4. Look at circles and how the area changes as the diameter increases. This can easily be given a meaningful context for students if applied to pizza sizes.
5. Explore the area:perimeter relationship in rectangles of different dimensions.

Solutions

The specials listed on the first student page do offer a genuine savings in terms of the cost to purchase the cakes listed, but there is always a flaw. For some of the specials, if the amount of money spent on the special were used to purchase a different cake (or cakes) at the regular price, the amount of cake received would be greater. For other specials, the cost for an equivalent amount of cake would be less.

Save $5 Specials

- Four basic cakes for $15
  Four basic cakes are equivalent to one large cake, which is only $10 at the regular price.
- Two large cakes for $15
  Two large cakes give you less cake than what you get in one family cake, which is the same price ($15).

- Three large cakes for $25
  Three large cakes gives you less cake than what you get in one party cake, and the party cake is $5 cheaper ($20).
- One large cake and one family cake for $20
  One large cake and one family cake gives you less cake than what you get in one party cake, and the party cake is the same price ($20).

Save $10 Specials

- Four large cakes for $30
  Four large cakes are equivalent to what you get in one party cake, but the party cake is $10 cheaper ($20).
- Two basic cakes, two large cakes, and two family cakes for $50
  Two party cakes give you more cake than what you get in this special, and cost $10 less ($40).

Identify the Better Deal

- One family cake or one large cake and one basic cake?
  One family cake gives you more for your money.
- One basic cake and one party cake or one large cake and one family cake?
  One party and one basic gives you more for your money.
- Two family cakes or one large cake and one party cake?
  One large and one party gives you more for your money.
- Two family cakes or two basic cakes and one party cake?
  These both give you the same amount of cake for the same price.
- Two party cakes or one party cake, one family cake, and one basic cake?
  Two party cakes gives you more cake for your money.

* Reprinted with permission from *Principles and Standards for School Mathematics*, 2000 by the National Council of Teachers of Mathematics. All rights reserved.

CALCULATING CAKE COSTS

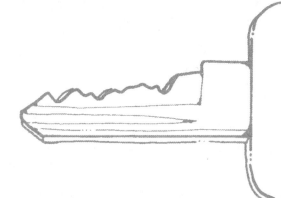

Key Question

Why are the "money-saving specials" not actually good deals?

Learning Goals

Students will:

1. evaluate the costs of cakes based on the amount of cake you get for your money,
2. determine why special "money-saving" deals are not actually deals, and
3. compare two cakes to determine which gives you the most for your money.

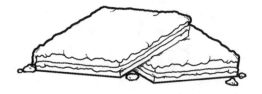

CALCULATING CAKE COSTS

Open-ended Version

All of the cakes at *Christina's Cake Creations* are exact squares. That means a 6" cake has sides of six inches all the way around. Christina's cake costs are fairly common, but her specials seem somewhat suspect. Use your sleuthing skills to find the flaws and determine the drawbacks of each "deal." Assume that it is always best to get the most cake for your money.

Christina's Cake Creations

	SAVE $5 SPECIALS	SAVE $10 SPECIALS
Basic Cakes $15.00	4 Large Cakes.............$30.00
Large Cakes...........$15.00	
Large Cakes..........$25.00	2 Basic Cakes,
Large Cake &	2 Large Cakes, &
Family Cake..........$20.00	2 Family Cakes $50.00

Party
24" cake

...e cakes to help you think about your answers. Use the
...e sure to address each special.

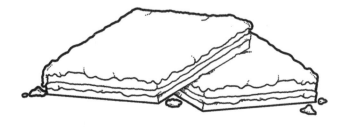

CALCULATING CAKE COSTS

Structured Version

All of the cakes at *Christina's Cake Creations* are exact squares. That means a 6" cake has sides of six inches all the way around. Christina's cake costs are fairly common, but her specials seem somewhat suspect. Use your sleuthing skills to find the flaws and determine the drawbacks of each "deal." Assume that it is always best to get the most cake for your money.

Christina's Cake Creations

PRICES	SAVE $5 SPECIALS	SAVE $10 SPECIALS
6" Basic Cake.............. $5.00	4 Basic Cakes $15.00	4 Large Cakes............. $30.00
12" Large Cake $10.00	2 Large Cakes...........$15.00	
18" Family Cake.......... $15.00	3 Large Cakes.......... $25.00	2 Basic Cakes,
24" Party Cake $20.00	1 Large Cake &	2 Large Cakes, &
	1 Family Cake.......... $20.00	2 Family Cakes $50.00

Cut out the scale models of the cakes and fill in the table below to help you with your answers. The table shows how many of each smaller cake it takes to make one larger cake. Some of the answers have been filled in for you. Show your work in the space below or on another sheet of paper. Be sure to address each special.

Cake Size	Number of smaller cakes in each larger cake		
	6"	12"	18"
12" square			
18" square		2.25	
24" square			1.78

CALCULATING CAKE COSTS

For each question, determine which of the two options gives you the most cake for your dollar using the standard prices from the first student page (not the specials). Show your work.

Which is a better deal, and why?

1. One family cake
    or
   One large cake and one basic cake

2. One basic cake and one party cake
    or
   One large cake and one family cake

3. Two family cakes
    or
   One large cake and one party cake

4. Two family cakes
    or
   Two basic cakes and one party cake

5. Two party cakes
    or
   One party cake, one family cake, and one basic cake

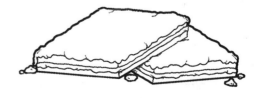

CALCULATING CAKE COSTS

Cut out these cake models to help you think about your answers.

Basic 6" cake	**Basic** 6" cake	**Large** 12" cake	**Large** 12" cake	**Large** 12" cake
Basic 6" cake	**Basic** 6" cake			
Basic 6" cake	**Basic** 6" cake	**Family** 18" cake		**Family** 18" cake
Large 12" cake				
Party 24" cake		**Party** 24" cake		

CALCULATING CAKE COSTS

Connecting Learning

1. What flaws are there in Christina's specials?

2. Which cake gives you the most for your money at the regular prices? Why?

3. Which cake gives you the least for your money at the regular prices? Why?

4. As the side lengths of a cake double, what happens to the area?

5. How many basic cakes would you have to buy to get the same amount of cake as a large? How much more would it cost you?

6. How many large and basic cakes would you have to buy to get the same amount of cake as a family? How much more would it cost you?

Problem-Solving Strategies
Look for Patterns

Patterns are everywhere. Some patterns repeat. Other patterns grow. Some patterns use numbers. Some patterns use shapes. Some patterns are cycles. Looking for patterns can help you solve problems. Sometimes, knowing the pattern and how to extend it gives you the answer.

Labor Day Dilemma

Topic
Patterns

Key Question
How many times will Wendy's birthday fall on Labor Day in her lifetime?

Learning Goals
Students will:
1. determine the number of times that September 6th falls on Labor Day from 1993 to 2093, and
2. look for patterns in their solutions.

Guiding Documents
Project 2061 Bechmark
- *Mathematics is the study of many kinds of patterns, including numbers and shapes and operations on them. Sometimes patterns are studied because they help to explain how the world works or how to solve practical problems, sometimes because they are interesting in themselves.*

NCTM Standards 2000*
- *Describe, extend, and make generalizations about geometric and numeric patterns*
- *Represent and analyze patterns and functions, using words, tables, and graphs*
- *Build new mathematical knowledge through problem solving*
- *Solve problems that arise in mathematics and in other contexts*
- *Apply and adapt a variety of appropriate strategies to solve problems*

Math
Pattern recognition
Problem solving

Integrated Processes
Observing
Recording
Comparing and contrasting
Generalizing
Applying

Problem-Solving Strategies
Look for patterns
Organize the information

Materials
Student pages

Background Information
Certain American holidays do not have a fixed date, but rather a fixed day. For example, President's Day is always the third Monday in February. Depending on the year, this could be anywhere from February 10th to 16th. People with birthdays around these fixed-day holidays find that they celebrate their birthdays on the holiday many times throughout their lives. This activity examines a scenario in which a girl's birthday is September 6th, which sometimes falls on Labor Day (the first Monday of September). The challenge is to determine the number of times in her life that she will celebrate her birthday on Labor Day. This involves exploring the patterns that occur in our calendar system and generalizing them to apply to the years in question. See *Solutions* for a full discussion of our calendar system and the patterns related to this activity.

Management
1. There are two different versions of this problem that can be given to students. The first version is completely open-ended and allows students to approach the problem any way they want. The second version provides students with a table to help them organize their findings and see the patterns. The discussion questions given can be used with both versions. Determine which version is most suited to your students and hand out the appropriate student pages.
2. Calendars for the month of September are provided for the years 1993 to 2000. This eight-year span should be enough for students to discover the patterns, making any other calendars unnecessary.

Procedure
1. Distribute the appropriate student page(s). If desired, have students get into groups.
2. Allow time for students to work on the problem and discover the patterns that will allow them to determine the solutions.
3. Have students share their solutions and discoveries.

Connecting Learning
1. What method(s) did you use to determine the number of times Wendy's birthday will be on Labor Day?
2. Describe the patterns that you discovered in the days and dates while doing this problem.
3. How are these patterns related to leap years?

4. Could you predict how many times Wendy's birthday would fall on a Friday throughout her life? How would you do that?
5. On what day of the week will your birthday be next year? How do you know?

Extensions

1. Look for patterns in the calendar system.
2. Modify the activity to be seasonally appropriate. (The principle will work for any holiday that is on a fixed day of the week each year. These holidays include President's Day (the third Monday in February), Memorial Day (the last Monday in May), and Thanksgiving (the last Thursday in November) among many others.) How many of the students in your class have a birthday that sometimes falls on one of these holidays? Were any of your students born on leap year day?
3. Explore other dating systems that have been tried before the one we use now.

Solutions

The calendar we use today has gone through a series of changes that have all attempted to make it as accurate as possible in relation to how long it takes the Earth to make one rotation around the sun. Because it takes approximately 365 ¼ days for the Earth to travel one time around the sun, we have years that are 365 days long with an extra day added every four years. These years with an extra day are known as "leap years." Even this adjustment is not perfect, however, because the extra ¼ of a day is actually just under six hours (which would be ¼ of a 24-hour day). To remedy this slight discrepancy in time, leap years are not instituted in century years that cannot be divided by 400 (1700, 1900, 2100, etc.).

All of that background is important in understanding the patterns that students will be discovering in this problem. What students should begin to realize as they study the problem is that the day of the week on which the sixth of September falls increases by one each successive year. Therefore, since the sixth was a Monday in 1993, it was a Tuesday in 1994, a Wednesday in 1995, and so on. Where this pattern changes is in the leap years. In every leap year, the day jumps two days of the week instead of just one. This breaks down into a pattern as shown below: (Leap years are listed in *italics*.)

Day of the week on which September 6th falls

1993: Monday	1997: Saturday
1994: Tuesday	1998: Sunday
1995: Wednesday	1999: Monday
1996: Friday	*2000: Wednesday*

As you can see, in the leap years, the day of the week skips ahead two. If the days of the week are numbered, it looks like this:

1 = Sunday, 2 = Monday, 3 = Tuesday,
4 = Wednesday, 5 = Thursday, 6 = Friday, 7 = Saturday

Day of the week on which September 6th falls

1993: 2	1997: 7	2001: 5	2005: 3	2009: 1
1994: 3	1998: 1	2002: 6	2006: 4	2010: 2
1995: 4	1999: 2	2003: 7	2007: 5	2011: 3
1996: 6	*2000: 4*	*2004: 2*	*2008: 7*	*2012: 5*

This pattern of increasing by one day for three years and then jumping two days in the leap years continues until you reach a century year that cannot be divided by 400. (The next time this will occur is 2100.)

Once students have discovered this larger pattern, it should be fairly easy for them to extend the pattern to determine the number of Labor Day birthdays in Wendy's entire life. Assuming she was born in 1993, by her 10th birthday, Wendy will have had two birthdays that fall on Labor Day (1993, 1999). By her 20th birthday, she will have had four birthdays on Labor Day (1993, 1999, 2004, 2010). By her 50th birthday, eight birthdays will have fallen on Labor Day ('93, '99, '04, '10, '21, '27, '32, '38), and by her 100th birthday, Wendy will have had a total of 15 birthdays on Labor Day (…'38, '49, '55, '60, '66, '77, '83, '88).

* Reprinted with permission from *Principles and Standards for School Mathematics*, 2000 by the National Council of Teachers of Mathematics. All rights reserved.

Labor Day Dilemma

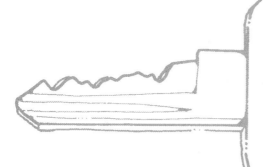

Key Question

How many times will Wendy's birthday fall on Labor Day in her lifetime?

Learning Goals

Students will:

1. determine the number of times that September 6th falls on Labor Day from 1993 to 2093, and
2. look for patterns in their solutions.

Labor Day Dilemma

Each of the calendars below is for the month of September. Labor Day is always the first Monday of the month, indicated by a star. Use these calendars to help you discover the patterns needed to solve the problem.

1993

S	M	T	W	Th	F	S
			1	2	3	4
5	☆6	7	8	9	10	11
12	13	14	15	16	17	18
19	20	21	22	23	24	25
26	27	28	29	30		

1994

S	M	T	W	Th	F	S
				1	2	3
4	☆5	6	7	8	9	10
11	12	13	14	15	16	17
18	19	20	21	22	23	24
25	26	27	28	29	30	

1995

S	M	T	W	Th	F	S
					1	2
3	☆4	5	6	7	8	9
10	11	12	13	14	15	16
17	18	19	20	21	22	23
24	25	26	27	28	29	30

1996

S	M	T	W	Th	F	S
1	☆2	3	4	5	6	7
8	9	10	11	12	13	14
15	16	17	18	19	20	21
22	23	24	25	26	27	28
29	30					

1997

S	M	T	W	Th	F	S
	☆1	2	3	4	5	6
7	8	9	10	11	12	13
14	15	16	17	18	19	20
21	22	23	24	25	26	27
28	29	30				

1998

S	M	T	W	Th	F	S
		1	2	3	4	5
6	☆7	8	9	10	11	12
13	14	15	16	17	18	19
20	21	22	23	24	25	26
27	28	29	30			

1999

S	M	T	W	Th	F	S
			1	2	3	4
5	☆6	7	8	9	10	11
12	13	14	15	16	17	18
19	20	21	22	23	24	25
26	27	28	29	30		

2000

S	M	T	W	Th	F	S
					1	2
3	☆4	5	6	7	8	9
10	11	12	13	14	15	16
17	18	19	20	21	22	23
24	25	26	27	28	29	30

Labor Day Dilemma

Wendy was born on September 6th, 1993. In 1993, Labor Day was celebrated on September 6th. In 1999, on her sixth birthday, Labor Day was on September 6th again. How many times will Wendy's birthday fall on Labor Day by her tenth birthday? …her twentieth birthday? …her fiftieth birthday? If Wendy lived to be 100 years old, how many times would her birthday have fallen on Labor Day throughout her life? Use the calendars provided to help you with your answers. Show your work below.

Labor Day Dilemma

Wendy was born on September 6th, 1993. In 1993, Labor Day was celebrated on September 6th. In 1999, on her sixth birthday, Labor Day was on September 6th again. How many times will Wendy's birthday fall on Labor Day by her tenth birthday? …her twentieth birthday? …her fiftieth birthday? If Wendy were to live to be 100 years old, how many times would her birthday fall on Labor Day throughout her life?

This table should help you answer these questions. Use the calendars provided to fill it in. Record your answers in the space below the table. You can use the back of the paper to show your work if necessary.

Year	Day of Week	Labor Day?	Leap Year?
1993	Monday	Yes	No
1994			
1995			
1996			
1997			
1998			
1999			

HAPPY BIRTH / LABOR DAY !

Labor Day Dilemma

1. What method(s) did you use to determine the number of times Wendy's birthday will be on Labor Day?

2. Describe the patterns that you discovered in the days and dates while doing this problem.

3. How are these patterns related to leap years?

4. Could you predict how many times Wendy's birthday would fall on a Friday throughout her life? How would you do that?

5. Based on what you learned in this activity, determine the day of the week on which your birthday will fall for the next five years.

Labor Day Dilemma

Connecting Learning

1. What method(s) did you use to determine the number of times Wendy's birthday will be on Labor Day?

2. Describe the patterns that you discovered in the days and dates while doing this problem.

3. How are these patterns related to leap years?

4. Could you predict how many times Wendy's birthday would fall on a Friday throughout her life? How would you do that?

5. On what day of the week will your birthday be next year? How do you know?

RULES OF ARRANGEMENT

Topic
Patterns

Key Question
What possible patterns could be represented with the sequences of shapes?

Learning Goals
Students will:
1. identify characteristics of a set of shapes and sort them by a variety of attributes;
2. examine a series of three shapes and identify three different patterns, or rules, that could define the sequence;
3. determine which of their remaining shapes could come next in the sequence given each of these rules; and
4. create their own patterns using the shapes.

Guiding Documents
Project 2061 Benchmark
• *Mathematics is the study of many kinds of patterns, including numbers and shapes and operations on them. Sometimes patterns are studied because they help to explain how the world works or how to solve practical problems, sometimes because they are interesting in themselves.*

NCTM Standards 2000*
• *Describe, extend, and make generalizations about geometric and numeric patterns*
• *Represent and analyze patterns and functions, using words, tables, and graphs*
• *Identify, compare, and analyze attributes of two- and three-dimensional shapes and develop vocabulary to describe the attributes*
• *Classify two- and three-dimensional shapes according to their properties and develop definitions of classes of shapes such as triangles and pyramids*
• *Build new mathematical knowledge through problem solving*

Math
Geometry
    2-D shapes
        properties
Patterns
Problem solving

Integrated Processes
Observing
Comparing and contrasting
Identifying
Analyzing
Generalizing
Applying

Problem-Solving Strategies
Look for patterns
Use manipulatives

Background Information
This activity has students explore patterning in a variety of ways with an emphasis on problem solving and multiple solutions. The context for the patterns is a variety of regular and irregular geometric shapes having three, four, five, or six sides. This makes these activities ripe for geometry extensions studying the properties and attributes of shapes.

Students will cut out a set of 16 shapes, and then explore these shapes by sorting them in a variety of ways. Once they have thoroughly explored the shapes, they will move on to a series of pattern explorations.

Management
1. Copy the page of shapes onto card stock. Each student will need one copy of this page.
2. This activity is divided into two parts. In the first, students explore characteristics of the shapes and sort them in various ways. In the second part, they are challenged to identify, define, extend, and create patterns using those shapes.
3. It is important that students are aware of all the attributes that can form the basis for patterns. Attributes include the relative size of the shapes, the fill of the shapes (solid, specks, pluses, dots), the kind of shape (triangle, quadrilateral, pentagon, hexagon), whether there is an odd or even number of sides, whether there are acute, right, or obtuse angles, and so on. It is also important that students understand that the pattern must repeat after four shapes. It may repeat in fewer than four, but may not be longer than four. The following tables give several examples of usable and unusable patterns.

Examples of usable patterns

Repeats after two	odd sides, even sides, odd sides, even sides…
Repeats after three	pluses, dots, specks, pluses, dots, specks…
Repeats after four	hexagon, pentagon, quadrilateral, triangle, hexagon, pentagon, quadrilateral, triangle…

Examples of unusable patterns

Repeats after five	solid, dots, pluses, pluses, specks, solid, dots, pluses, pluses, specks…
Repeats after six	triangle, quadrilateral, pentagon, pentagon, hexagon, pentagon, triangle, quadrilateral, pentagon, pentagon, hexagon, pentagon…

Procedure

1. Distribute the first student page and scissors to each student.
2. Have students cut out the 16 shapes and explore various ways to sort them. Encourage students to look at many different attributes of the shapes such as size, types of angles, number of sides, etc.
3. Conduct a time of class discussion in which students can share the observations they have made about the shapes. Students should discover that there are four different kinds of shapes: triangles, quadrilaterals, pentagons, and hexagons. There are also four different fills: solid, speckles, pluses, and dots. There is one of each shape with each fill. Some of the shapes are regular, while some are irregular.
4. Once this time of exploration and discussion is completed, distribute the second and third student pages and go over the instructions with the class.
5. Go over some of the attributes that can form the basis of patterns (see *Management 3*). Encourage creativity as students identify possible rules. Remind students that the patterns must repeat every four or fewer shapes.
6. Once students have completed these two pages, distribute the final student page.
7. Instruct students to trace around the shapes they have chosen for their patterns and do their best to draw the appropriate fill in each. Have them trade papers with a classmate and find rules for each other's patterns.
8. Close with a time of class discussion where students share about the patterns they developed and the things they learned from this activity.

Connecting Learning

1. What kinds of shapes are in your set? [triangles, rectangles, paralellograms, trapezoids, pentagons, hexagons]
2. What other things do you notice about your shapes? [they have different fills, some are regular, some are irregular, etc.]
3. What rules were you able to come up with for the patterns?
4. How do your rules compare to those your classmates developed?
5. What shapes did you use to make your own pattern? In what ways could that pattern be extended?
6. Why are there many possibilities for extending the pattern?
7. Could you develop a three-shape pattern that would have only one possible rule? Why or why not?

Extension

Follow this activity with *Perpetual Patterns*.

Key Question

What possible patterns could be represented with the sequences of shapes?

Learning Goals

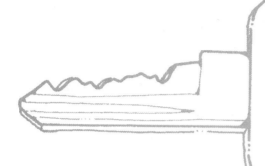

Students will:

1. identify characteristics of a set of shapes and sort them by a variety of attributes;
2. examine a series of three shapes and identify three different patterns, or rules, that could define the sequence;
3. determine which of their remaining shapes could come next in the sequence given each of these rules; and
4. create their own patterns using the shapes.

RULES OF ARRANGEMENT

Carefully cut out the shapes below. Sort them in at least three different ways. Record the results of each sort and describe the set of shapes as completely as you can. How many shapes are there? What kinds of shapes are there? How many fills are there? How many shapes are there with each fill? What kinds of shapes have each fill?

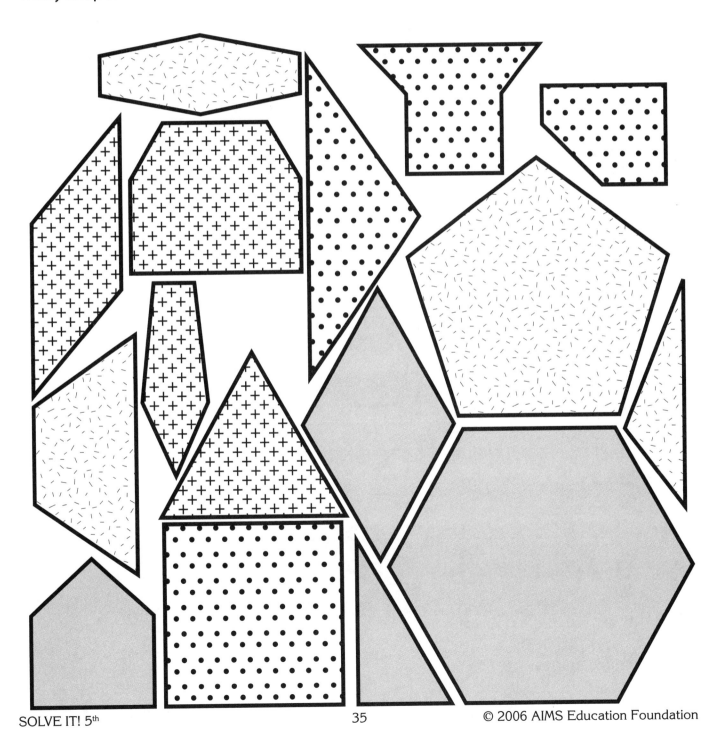

RULES OF ARRANGEMENT

In the sequences below and on the next page, there are several possible ways to continue the patterns using only the shapes you cut out. Find three different rules that could describe the patterns. List all of the possible next shapes based on those rules. Use the spaces provided to record the rule. Write or draw all of the possible next shapes. One problem has been done for you as an example.

Rule One: The rule is number of sides: triangle (3), quadrilateral (4), pentagon (5), hexagon (6)

Possible next shapes: Any hexagon

Rule Two: The rule is fills: speckles, pluses, solid, speckles, pluses, solid

Possible next shapes: Any speckled shape

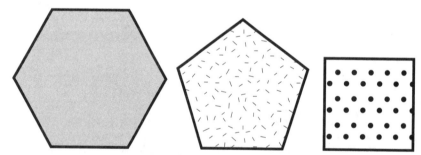

1.

Rule One: _____

Possible next shapes: _____

Rule Two: _____

Possible next shapes: _____

Rule Three: _____

Possible next shapes: _____

RULES OF ARRANGEMENT

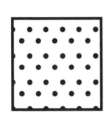 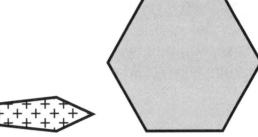

2.

Rule One: _____

Possible next shapes: _____

Rule Two: _____

Possible next shapes: _____

Rule Three: _____

Possible next shapes: _____

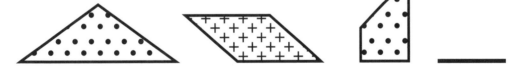

3.

Rule One: _____

Possible next shapes: _____

Rule Two: _____

Possible next shapes: _____

Rule Three: _____

Possible next shapes: _____

Use this page to create your own three-shape pattern that can be extended in at least three different ways. Illustrate your pattern by tracing around the shapes you have chosen and giving them the appropriate fill. Trade your paper with a classmate and have him/her find three different rules that could describe your pattern.

Connecting Learning

1. What kinds of shapes are in your set?

2. What other things do you notice about your shapes?

3. What rules were you able to come up with for the patterns?

4. How do your rules compare to those your classmates developed?

5. What shapes did you use to make your own pattern? In what ways could that pattern be extended?

6. Why are there many possibilities for extending the pattern?

7. Could you develop a three-shape pattern that would have only one possible rule? Why or why not?

PERPETUAL PATTERNS

Topic
Patterns

Key Question
How can you continue the pattern of shapes?

Learning Goals
Students will:
1. identify, sort, and explore a set of regular and irregular polygons;
2. use these shapes to play a pattern game; and
3. identify the shapes that can and cannot be used to fill in part of a missing pattern.

Guiding Documents
Project 2061 Benchmark
• *Mathematics is the study of many kinds of patterns, including numbers and shapes and operations on them. Sometimes patterns are studied because they help to explain how the world works or how to solve practical problems, sometimes because they are interesting in themselves.*

NCTM Standards 2000*
• *Describe, extend, and make generalizations about geometric and numeric patterns*
• *Identify, compare, and analyze attributes of two- and three-dimensional shapes and develop vocabulary to describe the attributes*
• *Classify two- and three-dimensional shapes according to their properties and develop definitions of classes of shapes such as triangles and pyramids*
• *Build new mathematical knowledge through problem solving*

Math
Geometry
  2-D shapes
Sorting
Pattern recognition
Problem solving

Integrated Processes
Observing
Comparing and contrasting
Organizing
Recording
Evaluating
Justifying

Problem-Solving Strategies
Look for patterns
Use manipulatives
Guess and check

Materials
Scissors
Game cards (see *Management 3*)
Student page
Transparency film (see *Management 5*)
Card stock

Background Information
This activity continues the exploration of patterns that was begun in *Rules of Arrangement*. Added to the shapes from that activity are an additional eight irregular polygons, giving students a set of 24 with which to work. These shapes are used to play a game in which the goal is to maintain a pattern for as long as possible. The challenge is, the pattern is never verbalized and can change with each card that is played.

Students are also assessed on their abilities to recognize all possible patterns in a sequence of shapes by identifying which shapes can and cannot fill in the missing space in the sequence. This is often how patterns are assessed on standardized tests.

Management
1. This activity is a continuation of *Rules of Arrangement*. Students must have done that activity before they will be able to complete this one. They will also need the shapes from *Rules of Arrangement*.
2. Copy the page of shapes onto card stock for durability. Each group needs one set.
3. To make the cards for the game, students can either glue their cutout shapes to 3" x 5" index cards, or cut out the set of cards provided. If the first option is taken, use glue sticks because this glue dries quickly and will not cause the shapes to bubble. If the second option is taken, the cards should be copied onto card stock and laminated for durability, if possible.
4. The rules of the game state that the patterns used must repeat after four or fewer cards. You may wish to raise this number to five after students have become comfortable with the game.
5. Make transparencies of the shape cards for use on the overhead in *Part Two* of the activity.

6. *Part Two* of the activity is divided into two sections and can function as an assessment. It may be done on a different day from *Part One*. The first section is individual and will give students practice with the way patterns are often tested on standardized tests. The second section is done as a class and requires students to use their problem-solving and communication skills.

Procedure

Part One

1. Have students get into groups of two, three, or four. Distribute one page of shapes to each group. Have students cut out the shapes and sort them in a variety of ways to become familiar with their attributes.
2. Ask one student from each group to add his or her set of shapes from *Rules of Arrangement* to the eight new shapes. Have students continue to sort and explore the entire set of 24 shapes.
3. After students have had a chance to share their discoveries about the new set of shapes, distribute the materials for the playing cards (see *Management 3)* and have students construct or cut out the cards.
4. Distribute the rules or put a copy of the rules page on the overhead. Go over the rules to the game as a class, playing several sample rounds to be sure that all students fully grasp the concept.
5. Allow groups time to play at least one or two full games before moving on to *Part Two*.

Part Two

1. Distribute the student page and have students complete it individually. Allow them to share and justify their answers.
2. Have students get back into their groups from *Part One* of the activity. Get out the transparencies of the shape cards.
3. Randomly select five shape cards and lay them out in a line on the overhead. Leave a blank space after the first card to mirror the space found on the student page.
4. Have groups pull those same five shape cards from their decks and lay them out in the same order, leaving the blank space after the first card.
5. Challenge groups to sort all of their remaining shape cards into two categories: those that can fill the blank space in the sequence and those that cannot.
6. When groups are finished, have one group share their sort with the class. If there are differences between group responses, discuss each of these individually. Try to determine as a class the most accurate sort.
7. Repeat this process as many times as desired.

Connecting Learning

1. What kinds of patterns did you use as you played the game?
2. Did you find that everyone began to use the same pattern, or did each person have a different idea of what the pattern was?
3. Did the game most often end with a challenge or with someone not being able to play a card? Why do you think this was so?
4. How were you able to determine which shapes could and could not go in the missing space on the student page?
5. Did everyone agree on how to sort the shapes when we tried the problems as a class? What were the reasons for any differences?
6. What would happen if the pattern could repeat after five shapes instead of four? Would that change how you sorted the shapes? Why or why not?

Solutions

Following are the problems from the student page. In each case, the shape that CANNOT fill in the blank space has been circled. Following each problem are explanations of some of the patterns that could justify the use of the other three shapes. Not every possible pattern has been mentioned in each case.

1.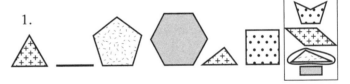

- The dotted pentagon could be next if the pattern is based on the fill (pluses, dots, specks, solid, pluses, dots...).
- Either the quadrilateral with pluses or the solid rectangle could be next if the pattern is based on the shape (triangle, quadrilateral, pentagon, hexagon, triangle, quadrilateral...).

2.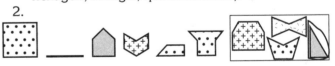

- Either the hexagon with pluses or the speckled hexagon could be next if the pattern is based on the shape (quadrilateral, hexagon, pentagon, hexagon, quadrilateral, hexagon...).
- The speckled hexagon could be next if the pattern is based on convex or concave shapes (convex, concave, convex...).
- The dotted pentagon could be next if the pattern is based on the fill (dots, dots, solid, pluses, dots, dots...).

3.

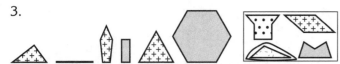

- The dotted hexagon could be next if the pattern is based on the shape (triangle, hexagon, pentagon, quadrilateral, triangle, hexagon...).
- The quadrilateral with pluses could be next if the pattern is based on odd or even number of sides (odd, even, odd, even...).
- The solid pentagon could be next if the pattern is based on the fill (pluses, solid, pluses, solid...).

4.

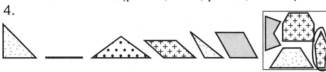

- The solid pentagon could be next if the pattern is based on the fill (specks, solid, dots, pluses, specks, solid...).
- The hexagon with pluses could be next if the pattern is based on odd or even number of sides (odd, even, odd, even...).
- The speckled quadrilateral could be next if the pattern is based on the shape (triangle, quadrilateral, triangle, quadrilateral...).

5.

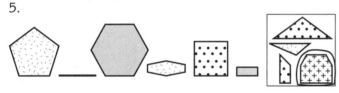

- The dotted triangle could be next if the pattern is based on the fill (specks, dots, solid, specks, dots, solid...).
- The speckled triangle or the dotted quadrilateral could be next if the pattern is based on relative size (bigger, smaller, bigger, smaller...).

* Reprinted with permission from *Principles and Standards for School Mathematics*, 2000 by the National Council of Teachers of Mathematics. All rights reserved.

PERPETUAL PATTERNS

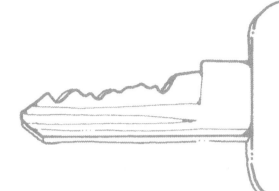

Key Question

How can you continue the pattern of shapes?

Learning Goals

Students will:

1. identify, sort, and explore a set of regular and irregular polygons;
2. use these shapes to play a pattern game; and
3. identify the shapes that can and cannot be used to fill in part of a missing pattern.

PERPETUAL PATTERNS

Players: Two, three, or four

Object: To maintain a pattern in the cards that are laid down.

The Game:

1. Deal out the cards so that every player has the same number. Cards should be held in the hand and not shown to the other player(s).

2. Player to the left of the dealer begins by laying down any card.

3. Play continues in a clockwise direction, with each player laying down one card per turn to the right of the card(s) already laid down, forming a straight line of cards where each is visible.

4. Every card played must fit into a pattern with the previous cards. Patterns must repeat after *four or fewer* cards.

   Examples of acceptable patterns (using fills):
   - specks, solid, specks solid…
   - dots, pluses, specks, dots, pluses, specks…
   - dots pluses, solid, specks, dots, pluses, solid, specks…

   Examples of unacceptable patterns (using fills):
   - pluses, specks, dots, dots, solid, pluses, specks, dots, dots, solid…
   - specks, specks, solid, solid, dots, dots, specks, specks, solid, solid, dots, dots…
   - dots, specks, specks, pluses, dots, solid, dots, specks, specks, pluses, dots, solid…

5. Patterns may be based on any characteristic of the shapes. Characteristics include, but are not limited to: relative size, shape, fill, odd or even number of sides, and concave or convex shapes.

6. When a player lays down a card that does not appear to follow any pattern, a challenge should occur. The challenge ends that game, and the winner is awarded 100 points.

7. In the event that no challenge occurs and a pattern recognized by all players is established, the game ends when any player can no longer play a card that fits the established pattern. When this happens, the game is a draw, and no points are awarded.

8. If all players are able to use all of their cards to follow the established pattern, each player receives 100 points.

9. The first player to reach 500 points is the winner.

Challenges: A player may be challenged only after he/she has laid down a card, and before the next player has laid down a card. The challenger may be any other player. When challenged, a player must explain the pattern that he/she sees in the cards and justify how the card that he/she just played fits that pattern. If a valid pattern exists and is described accurately, the challenged player wins. If the pattern is invalid, or does not exist, the challenger wins.

A sample game is described and illustrated here, beginning with the third card played.

After the first three cards have been played, the number of possible patterns is high.

Some of the possible patterns:

*   Relative size: larger, smaller, larger
*   Shape: triangle, quadrilateral, pentagon
*   Fill: specks, solid, dots
*   Odd/Even: odd, even, odd
*   Convex/concave: convex, convex, concave

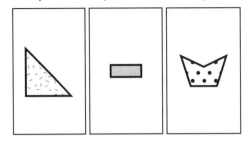

The choice of the fourth card eliminates the possibility of a relative size pattern, but several other patterns are still possible.

Some of the possible patterns:

*   Shape: triangle, quadrilateral, pentagon, hexagon
*   Fill: specks, solid, dots, pluses
*   Odd/Even: odd, even, odd, even
*   Convex/concave: convex, convex, concave, concave

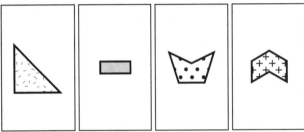

After the fifth card is played the fill possibility is eliminated, but there are still at least three other possible patterns.

Some of the possible patterns:

*   Shape: triangle, quadrilateral, pentagon, hexagon, triangle
*   Odd/Even: odd, even, odd, even, odd
*   Convex/concave: convex, convex, concave, concave, convex

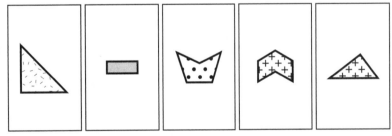

Even after the sixth card is played the pattern is not completely set. At least two different patterns are still possible.

Some of the possible patterns:

*   Odd/Even: odd, even, odd, even, odd, even
*   Convex/concave: convex, convex, concave, concave, convex, convex

PERPETUAL PATTERNS

Copy these shapes onto card stock and distrubute one set to each group.

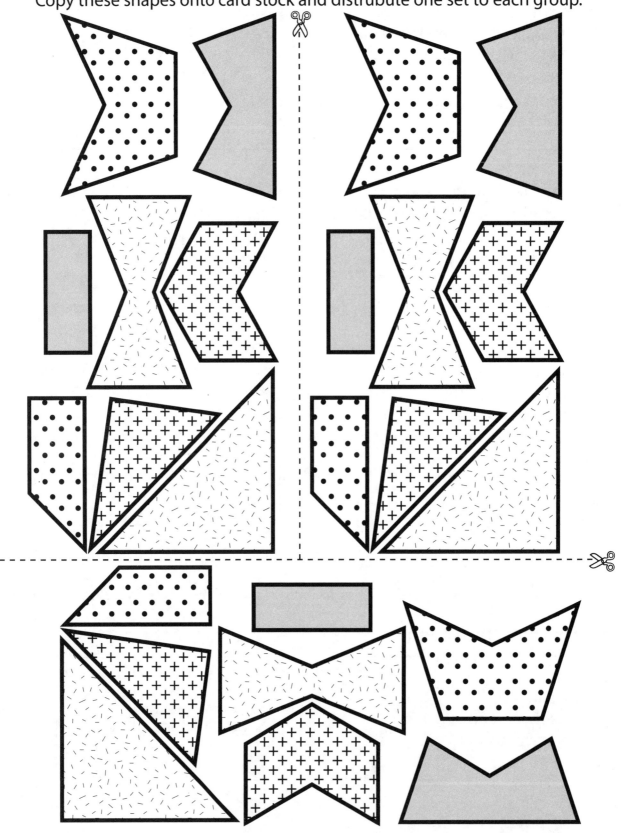

PERPETUAL PATTERNS

Examine the patterns below. In each case, circle the shape in the rectangle on the right that can NOT fill in the blank in the sequence. Patterns can be based on relative size, shape, fill, odd or even number of sides, or convex or concave. Patterns will always repeat after *four or fewer* shapes.

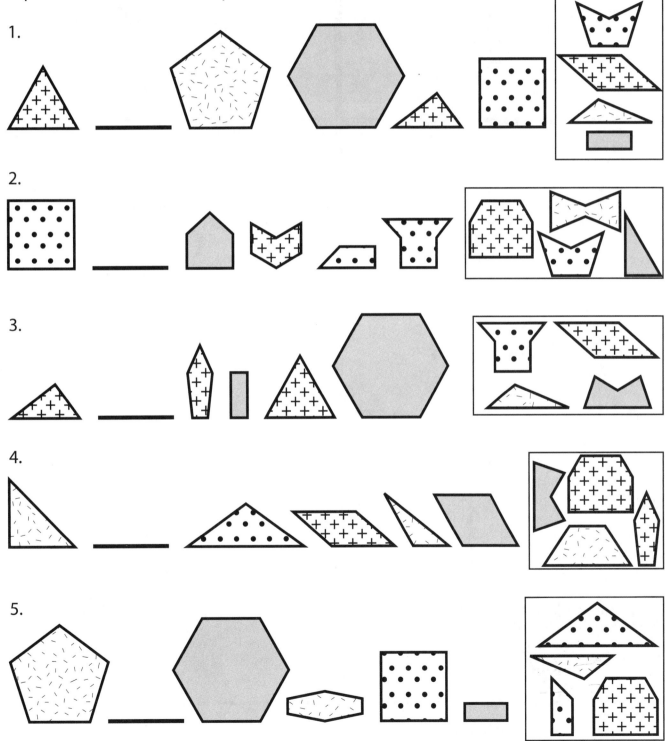

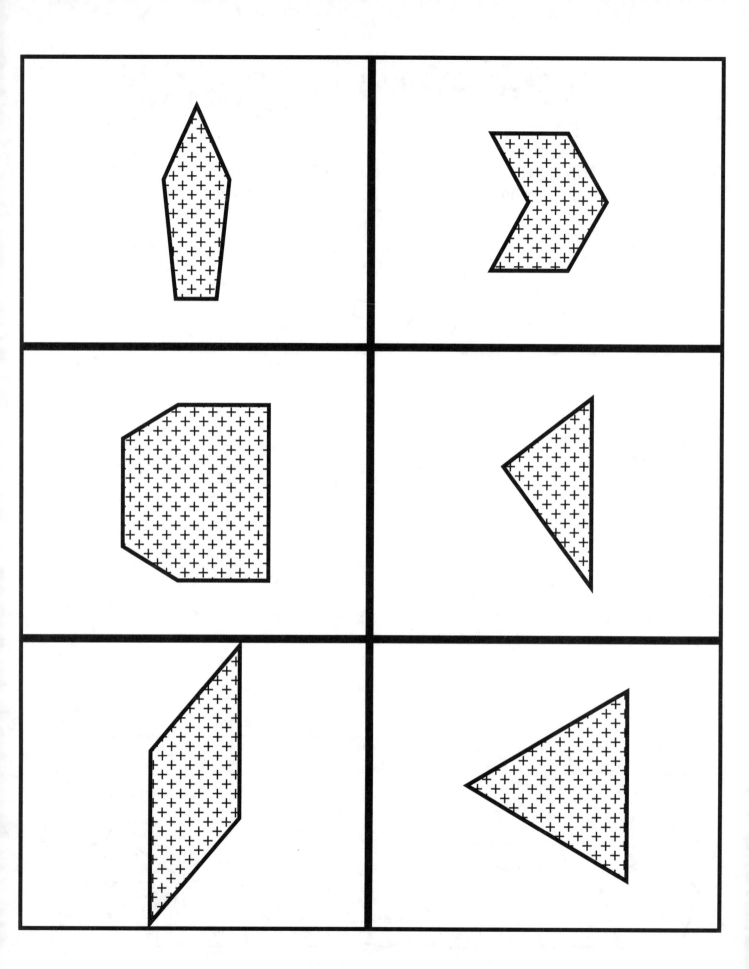

48

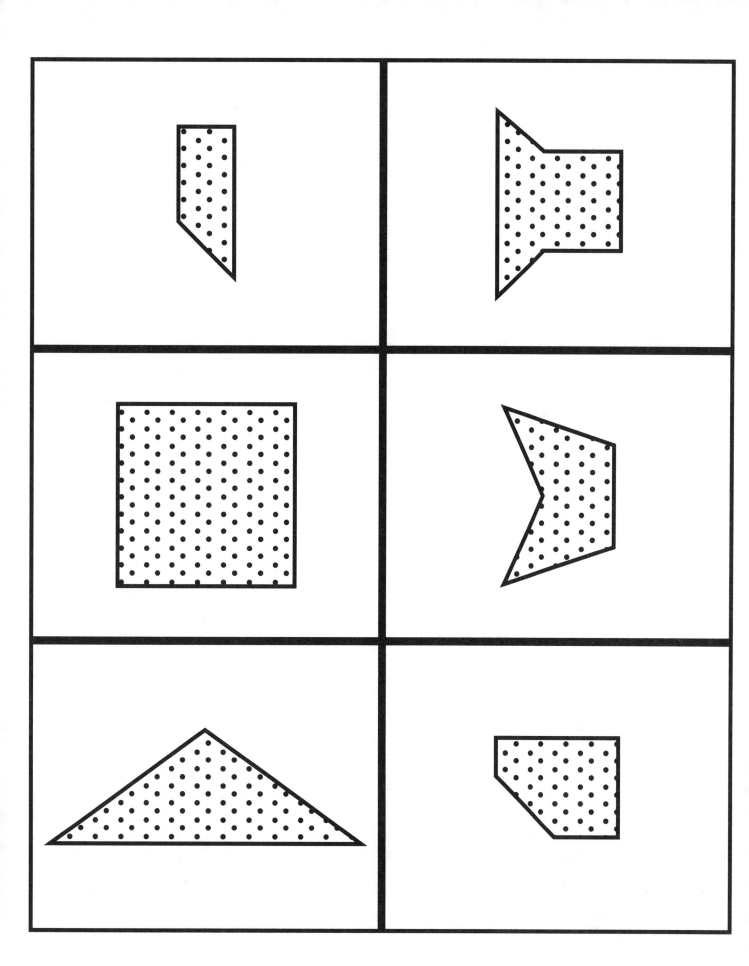

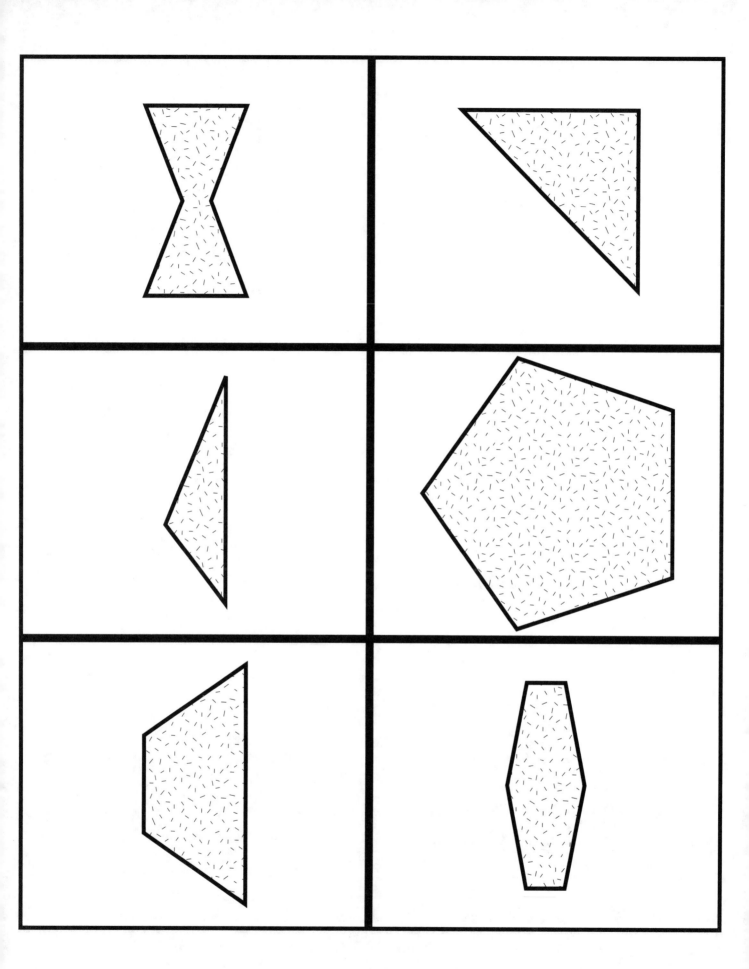

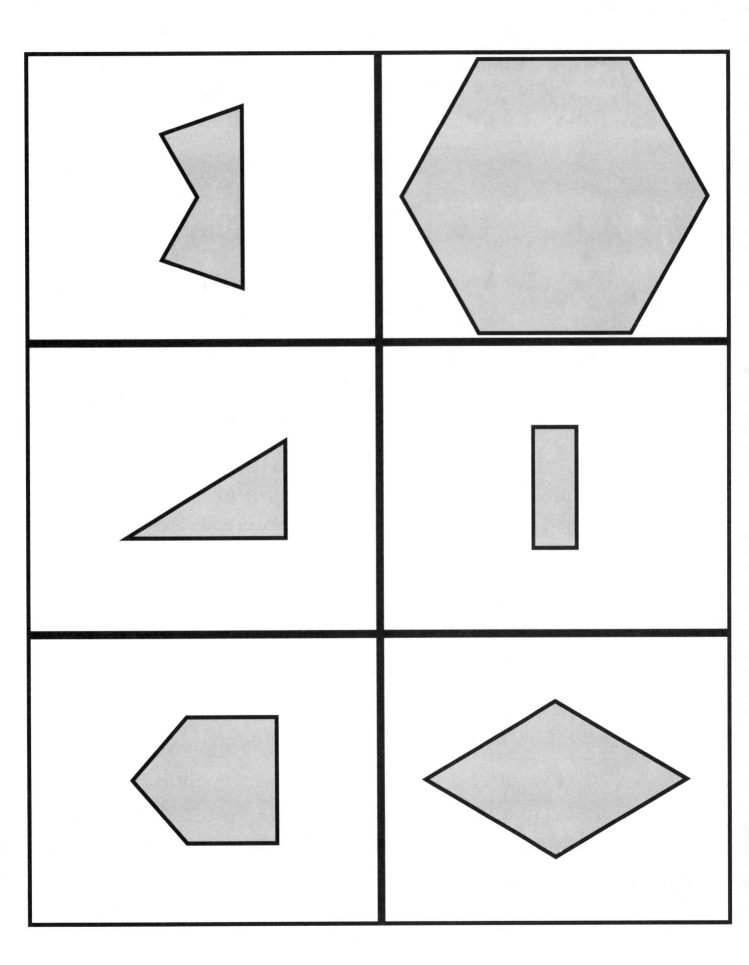

Connecting Learning

1. What kinds of patterns did you use as you played the game?

2. Did you find that everyone began to use the same pattern, or did each person have a different idea of what the pattern was?

3. Did the game most often end with a challenge or with someone not being able to play a card? Why do you think this was so?

4. How were you able to determine which shapes could and could not go in the missing space on the student page?

5. Did everyone agree on how to sort the shapes when we tried the problems as a class? What were the reasons for any differences?

6. What would happen if the pattern could repeat after five shapes instead of four? Would that change how you sorted the shapes? Why or why not?

Problem-Solving Strategies
Work Backwards

Sometimes it's best to start at the finish when solving a problem. Working backwards helps when you know the answer, but don't know how to get there. You can start at the end and find the missing steps to get to the beginning.

Counting the Miles

Topic
Problem solving

Key Question
How many miles did the Martinez family travel each day?

Learning Goal
Students will solve a multi-step word problem to determine the number of miles traveled by the Martinez family each day.

Guiding Document
NCTM Standards 2000*
- *Build new mathematical knowledge through problem solving*
- *Solve problems that arise in mathematics and in other contexts*
- *Apply and adapt a variety of appropriate strategies to solve problems*
- *Monitor and reflect on the process of mathematical problem solving*

Math
Problem solving

Integrated Processes
Observing
Comparing and contrasting
Recording
Applying

Problem-Solving Strategies
Work backwards
Organize the information
Guess and check

Materials
Student page

Background Information
This activity is a multi-step word problem that can be solved in several different ways. While problems like this are often found in algebra classes because they lend themselves to being solved algebraically, many can also be done arithmetically if other problem-solving techniques like looking for patterns, making a table, or

working backwards are used. In this activity, students are challenged to solve the following problem:

The Martinez family went on a 500-mile car trip that took five days. To make the drive more enjoyable, the family drove a short distance the first day. The second day they added 20 miles to the first day's distance. On each following day they added 20 miles to the previous day's distance. How many miles did the family travel each day?

Management
1. Students should work together in small groups.
2. An optional challenge problem is included at the bottom of the student page. This problem can be used as an assessment to see what students learned while working on the initial problem.

Procedure
1. Have students get into groups and distribute the student page.
2. Read through the problem together as a class and allow groups time to find a solution.
3. Have groups share their solutions and the problem-solving strategies they used to reach these solutions.
4. If desired, have students complete the additional challenge.

Connecting Learning
1. How many miles did the Martinez family travel each day?
2. What methods did you use to find this answer?
3. How do your group's strategies compare to the strategies used by other groups?

Solutions
One way to approach this problem is to use averages. The arithmetic mean of the distance traveled each day is easily found by dividing the total distance by the number of days. This gives an average daily distance of 100 miles. Armed with this average, and the knowledge that there is a uniform difference of 20 miles between each day's mileage, each day's distance can be found. Whenever five equally spaced numbers are ordered from smallest to largest, the middle number is not only the median (another form of average), it is also the mean. This indicates that the arithmetic mean

of 100 miles is the distance traveled on the third day. Each subsequent day's trip is 20 miles further and each previous day's trip is 20 miles shorter. Thus, by going backwards and forwards from this middle number, the distances for each day can be found. These distances are 60 miles for the first day, 80 miles for the second day, 100 miles for the third day, 120 miles for the fourth day, and 140 miles for the fifth day. To see if the solution is correct, these five distances must be added to see if they have a sum of 500. Since this is the case, the problem has been solved correctly.

Another way to solve this problem is to start with the information given—that 20 additional miles are traveled each day. Using this knowledge, it is possible to work backwards, in several steps, to find the original distance traveled on the first day. The following table shows the first step in this process—finding the total extra distance traveled on the second through fifth days.

Day	1	2	3	4	5	Total additional miles
Additional miles	0	20	40	60	80	200

From this information, work backwards to find the distance traveled on the first day. To do this, first subtract the total number of additional miles (200) for days two through five from the total trip distance (500 miles). This gives a difference of 300 miles for the five days. Next, divide the 300 miles by five days to find the original day's distance of 60 miles. Now that the first day's distance is known, all that is left is to add the base miles to the additional miles for days two through five. This information is presented in the following table.

Day	1	2	3	4	5	Totals
Base distance in miles	60	60	60	60	60	300
Additional distance in miles	0	20	40	60	80	200
Day's distance in miles	60	80	100	120	140	500

* Reprinted with permission from *Principles and Standards for School Mathematics*, 2000 by the National Council of Teachers of Mathematics. All rights reserved.

Counting the Miles

Key Question

How many miles did the Martinez family travel each day?

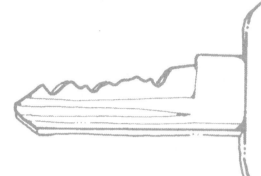

Learning Goal

Students will:

solve a multi-step word problem to determine the number of miles traveled by the Martinez family each day.

The Martinez family went on a 500-mile car trip that took five days. To make the drive more enjoyable, the family drove a short distance the first day. The second day they added 20 miles to the first day's distance. On each following day they added 20 miles to the previous day's distance.

How many miles did the family travel each day?

Show your work in the space below. Be ready to share your problem-solving strategies with others in the class.

Challenge: Using what you learned from the above problem, find the number of miles traveled each day for a 10-day trip of 1,000 miles using the same travel plan—driving a short distance the first day and then adding 20 miles to each previous day's distance. Show your work on the back of this page.

Counting the Miles

Denver	583 miles
Dallas	450 miles
Durango	550 miles

Connecting Learning

CONNECTING LEARNING

1. How many miles did the Martinez family travel each day?

2. What methods did you use to find this answer?

3. How do your group's strategies compare to the strategies used by other groups?

COVER-UPS

Topic
Problem solving

Key Question
How can you cover squares in each grid so that the remaining numbers in each of the rows and columns have a sum of 10?

Learning Goal
Students will cover one or more squares in each row and column of a square grid so that the remaining numbers in each row and column have a sum of 10.

Guiding Document
NCTM Standards 2000*
- *Build new mathematical knowledge through problem solving*
- *Solve problems that arise in mathematics and in other contexts*
- *Apply and adapt a variety of appropriate strategies to solve problems*
- *Monitor and reflect on the process of mathematical problem solving*

Math
Number and operations
    addition
    combinations
Problem solving

Integrated Processes
Observing
Comparing and contrasting
Recording
Analyzing

Problem-Solving Strategies
Work backwards
Guess and check
Use manipulatives
Write a number sentence

Materials
Area Tiles or small marking chips
Student pages

Background Information
This activity is a modification of "Crossout" from the April 2006 *Games* magazine. Square grids of different sizes are filled with numbers. The challenge is to cover one or more squares in each row and column so that the remaining numbers in each row and column have a specific sum. By adding the use of a manipulative and providing challenges at different levels of difficulty, the problem has been made appropriate for elementary students.

Management
1. Students will need Area Tiles or similar small chips that they can use to cover the spaces on the student pages. Pennies, beans, or buttons all work. For *Part One*, each student needs four marking chips. For *Part Two*, 10 chips are needed. For *Part Three*, 12 chips per student are necessary.
2. There are three parts to this activity, each one increasing in difficulty. You may wish to use only the first one or two parts instead of all three.

Procedure
1. Distribute the first student page and marking chips to each student.
2. Go over the instructions and the example as a class to make sure that everyone understands the challenge.
3. Give students time to find solutions and record them by shading in the covered squares in each grid.
4. Repeat with the additional challenges, if desired.
5. Close with a time of class discussion where students share their solutions, the problem-solving strategies they used, and what they learned.

Connecting Learning
1. What three-number combinations remained after you covered the squares in the first grid? [6 + 1 + 1, 5 + 2 + 1, 4 + 3 + 1, 3 + 3 + 2]
2. Are these all of the possible three-number combinations that have a sum of eight? Which one is missing? [4 + 2 + 2]
3. What three-number combinations remained after you covered the squares in the second grid? [6 + 3 + 1, 6 + 2 + 2, 5 + 4 + 1, 5 + 3 + 2, 4 + 4 + 2, 4 + 3 + 3]
4. Are these all of the possible three-number combinations that have a sum of 10? Which ones are missing? [8 + 1 + 1, 7 + 2 + 1]
5. What are all of the four-number combinations that have a sum of 10? [7 + 1 + 1 + 1, 6 + 2 + 1 + 1, 5 + 3 + 1 + 1, 5 + 2 + 2 + 1, 4 + 4 + 1 + 1, 4 + 3 + 2 + 1, 3 + 3 + 3 + 1, 3 + 3 + 2 + 2]
6. Which ones of these were used in the grid for *Part Two? ...Part Three?*

7. What problem-solving strategies did you use as you solved these problems?
8. If you had another similar problem to solve, would you do anything differently? Why or why not?

Extension

Challenge students to create their own grids for classmates to solve. It will be easier if students do this by manipulating slips of paper with numbers written on them until they find an arrangement that works. Then they can record the numbers in a grid and fill in the extra numbers.

Solutions

Part One

3	1	2	4
2	6	1	1
3	1	2	3
2	1	5	4

3 + 1 + 4 = 8
6 + 1 + 1 = 8
3 + 2 + 3 = 8
2 + 1 + 5 = 8

```
  3   1   1   4
  3   6   2   1
+ 2 + 1 + 5 + 3
  8   8   8   8
```

2	1	4	4
7	6	3	1
3	2	2	5
5	2	3	1

4 + 4 + 2 = 10
6 + 3 + 1 = 10
3 + 2 + 5 = 10
5 + 2 + 3 = 10

```
  2   6   4   4
  3   2   3   1
+ 5 + 2 + 3 + 5
 10  10  10  10
```

Part Two

2	4	3	1	4
2	1	2	3	4
1	7	1	1	1
5	1	3	2	1
6	1	3	5	1

2 + 3 + 1 + 4 = 10
2 + 1 + 3 + 4 = 10
1 + 7 + 1 + 1 = 10
5 + 1 + 3 + 1 = 10
1 + 3 + 5 + 1 = 10

```
  2   1   3   1   4
  2   7   1   3   4
  1   1   3   1   1
+ 5 + 1 + 3 + 5 + 1
 10  10  10  10  10
```

Part Three

6	2	2	1	1	2
4	7	1	1	2	1
2	1	3	2	3	4
3	1	5	3	6	1
1	5	2	1	3	4
1	1	3	5	3	3

6 + 2 + 1 + 1 = 10
7 + 1 + 1 + 1 = 10
2 + 1 + 3 + 4 = 10
1 + 5 + 3 + 1 = 10
1 + 2 + 3 + 4 = 10
1 + 1 + 5 + 3 = 10

```
  6   7   2   1   1   1
  2   1   1   1   3   4
  1   1   5   3   3   1
+ 1 + 1 + 2 + 5 + 3 + 4
 10  10  10  10  10  10
```

COVER-UPS

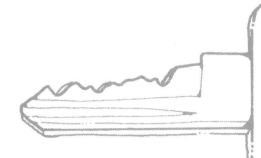

Key Question

How can you cover squares in each grid so that the remaining numbers in each of the rows and columns have a sum of 10?

Learning Goal

Students will:

cover one or more squares in each row and column of a square grid so that the remaining numbers in each row and column have a sum of 10.

TOP SECRET

　　　　　　61

COVER-UPS

In this example, one number from each row and column has been covered. The sum of the three numbers left in each row and column is six.

3	1	2	3
2	**2**	3	1
3	2	1	**3**
1	3	**1**	2

Your challenge is to cover one number in each row and column. The remaining three numbers in each row and column must add up to eight. Show your solution by shading in the covered squares.

3	**1**	**2**	**4**
2	**6**	**1**	**1**
3	**1**	**2**	**3**
2	**1**	**5**	**4**

Now, try to cover one number in each row and column so that numbers left add up to 10. Show your solution by shading in the covered squares.

2	**1**	**4**	**4**
7	**6**	**3**	**1**
3	**2**	**2**	**5**
5	**2**	**3**	**1**

COVER-UPS

Cover one number in each row and column. The remaining four numbers in each row and column must add up to 10. Show your solution by shading in the covered squares

3	1	3	2	2
1	1	2	6	2
1	7	1	1	1
3	1	4	2	3
3	1	3	1	5

63

## PART THREE

COVER-UPS

Cover two numbers in each row and column. The remaining four numbers in each row and column must add up to 10. Show your solution by shading in the covered squares.

6	2	2	1	1	2
4	7	1	1	2	1
2	1	3	2	3	4
3	1	5	3	6	1
1	5	2	1	3	4
1	1	3	5	3	3

64

COVER-UPS

Connecting Learning

1. What three-number combinations remained after you covered the squares in the first grid?

2. Are these all of the possible three-number combinations that have a sum of eight? Which one is missing?

3. What three-number combinations remained after you covered the squares in the second grid?

4. Are these all of the possible three-number combinations that have a sum of 10? Which ones are missing?

5. What are all of the four-number combinations that have a sum of 10?

6. Which ones of these were used in the grid for *Part Two? ...Part Three?*

7. What problem-solving strategies did you use as you solved these problems?

8. If you had another similar problem to solve, would you do anything differently? Why or why not?

Topic
Problem solving

Key Question
How can you help Charlie determine where to return his items and which credit card charges aren't his?

Learning Goals
Students will:
1. use their problem-solving skills to determine at which store two items were purchased, and
2. find the fraudulent charges on a credit card statement.

Guiding Document
NCTM Standards 2000*
- *Build new mathematical knowledge through problem solving*
- *Solve problems that arise in mathematics and in other contexts*
- *Apply and adapt a variety of appropriate strategies to solve problems*
- *Monitor and reflect on the process of mathematical problem solving*

Math
Number and operations
   decimal addition
Problem solving

Integrated Processes
Observing
Comparing and contrasting
Recording
Analyzing

Problem-Solving Strategies
Work backwards
Guess and check

Materials
Student pages

Background Information
The problem-solving skill of working backwards can be very useful when you know the end result but not how that result was achieved. In this activity, students are presented with scenarios involving money in which they must determine what was purchased at various stores as well as what charges are fraudulent. These multi-step word problems will give students valuable practice in reading problems, identifying necessary information, and applying the relevant information to solve the problem.

Management
1. This activity consists of two separate but related problems. They can be done together or each on different days.
2. Students can work on the problems individually or in small groups.

Procedure
1. Distribute the first student page and go over the challenge.
2. Allow time for students or groups to work out the solutions.
3. Discuss the solutions students discovered and the methods they used to arrive at these solutions.
4. Repeat this process with the second student page.

Connecting Learning
Part One
1. Which items did Charlie buy at Mega Mart? [toothpaste, shampoo, soap, laundry detergent, floor cleaner, mop, potted plant] ...Super Shop? [sneakers, CD, plant food] How do you know?
2. Where does Charlie need to return the mop? [Mega Mart] ...the sneakers? [Super Shop]
3. Are there other combinations of items that total $40.00? [sneakers, shampoo, soap, mop] How do you know that Charlie did not buy all of these items at Super Shop? [The number of items is wrong. He bought three items at one store and seven items at the other, not four and six.]
4. Are there other combinations of items that total $36.50? [plant, mop, CD, laundry detergent] How do you know that Charlie did not buy all of

these items at Mega Mart? [The number of items is wrong. He bought three items at one store and seven items at the other, not four and six.]

5. How did you go about solving this problem?

Part Two
1. What was the first thing you needed to do in order to solve this problem? [find out how much he was overcharged]
2. How much was Charlie overcharged by the credit card company? [$34.50]
3. What did you do with this information?
4. For which items should Charlie not have been charged? [Gas 'n' Grub—$30.00 and Grocery Garden $4.50] How do you know?

Extensions
1. Allow students to make up their own similar challenges to trade with classmates.
2. Change the amount that Charlie spent and the number of transactions he made and have students determine which charges should be removed.

* Reprinted with permission from *Principles and Standards for School Mathematics*, 2000 by the National Council of Teachers of Mathematics. All rights reserved.

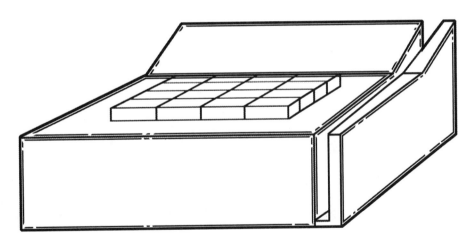

Credit *My Account*

5555 5555 5555 5555
Charlie

Key Question
How can you help Charlie determine where to return his items and which credit card charges aren't his?

Learning Goals

Students will:

1. use their problem-solving skills to determine at which store two items were purchased, and
2. find the fraudulent charges on a credit card statement.

Charlie went shopping at Mega Mart and Super Shop. He bought three items at one store and seven items at the other. He wants to return two items, but he can't remember where he bought them. He knows the cost of each item and how much he spent at each store. Help him figure out where to return each item.

Charlie wants to return the mop and the sneakers. He spent $36.50 at Mega Mart. He spent $40.00 at Super Shop.

5555 5555 5555 5555

Charlie

Someone has been using Charlie's credit card number illegally. Every month, he keeps track of how much he has spent. But, he doesn't write down where he spent the money. He knows that in month of April, he made 15 charges that totaled $237.00. His statement shows that he owes $271.50. Help Charlie find the fraudulent charges.

Description	Date	Amount
Gas 'n' Grub	4/05	$36.00
Grocery Garden	4/07	$58.00
Carbucks Coffee Company	4/07	$4.00
Mega Mart	4/09	$12.50
Sub Club Sandwiches	4/10	$5.50
Gas 'n' Grub	4/11	$30.00
Eat 'n' Run Burgers	4/12	$5.00
Carbucks Coffee Company	4/13	$4.00
Grocery Garden	4/14	$24.00
Produce Palace	4/14	$16.00
Carbucks Coffee Company	4/16	$4.00
Gas 'n' Grub	4/17	$31.50
Grocery Garden	4/18	$4.50
Carbucks Coffee Company	4/20	$4.00
Maria's Mexican Food	4/22	$18.50
Mega Mart	4/23	$10.00
Carbucks Coffee Company	4/27	$4.00
	Total Due	$271.50

Connecting Learning

Part One

1. Which items did Charlie buy at Mega Mart? ...Super Shop? How do you know?

2. Where does Charlie need to return the mop? ...the sneakers?

3. Are there other combinations of items that total $40.00? How do you know that Charlie did not buy all of these items at Super Shop?

4. Are there other combinations of items that total $36.50? How do you know that Charlie did not buy all of these items at Mega Mart?

5. How did you go about solving this problem?

Part Two

1. What was the first thing you needed to do in order to solve this problem?

2. How much was Charlie overcharged by the credit card company?

3. What did you do with this information?

4. For which items should Charlie not have been charged? How do you know?

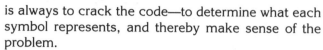

Topic
Problem solving

Key Question
How can you substitute a number for each letter in the problems so that the resulting addition problem is true?

Learning Goal
Students will solve simple cryptograms by replacing letters with the digits zero through nine so that the resulting addition problems are true.

Guiding Document
NCTM Standards 2000*
- *Build new mathematical knowledge through problem solving*
- *Solve problems that arise in mathematics and in other contexts*
- *Apply and adapt a variety of appropriate strategies to solve problems*
- *Monitor and reflect on the process of mathematical problem solving*

Math
Number and operations
    addition
Problem solving

Integrated Processes
Observing
Comparing and contrasting
Inferring
Applying

Problem-Solving Strategies
Work backwards
Guess and check
Use logical thinking

Materials
Student pages

Background Information
Those familiar with common pencil and paper puzzles will recognize the cryptograms explored in this activity. Cryptograms, as they are often called, take a variety of forms, but all include some kind of code—symbols (letters, numbers, etc.) that stand for something else. The challenge in a cryptogram is always to crack the code—to determine what each symbol represents, and thereby make sense of the problem.

This activity is one type of cryptogram. In this case, two addition problems are presented: one + one = two, and two + two + two = six. In each of these problems, a digit from zero to nine can be substituted for each of the letters so that the numbers form a correct addition problem. These particular puzzles were found in *Wonderful Ideas*, Vol. XII, No. 3, but they are merely two of an almost infinite number of possible problems that use the same technique.

At first glance, it might appear that these puzzles are purely trial and error and have little mathematical content or value; however, a closer look reveals problems rich in logical thinking and problem solving. By analyzing the outcomes of various number combinations, it is easy to eliminate many possibilities and quickly narrow the scope of the problem. For example, because the sum of any number plus itself is always even, the ones place digit in the sum of the first problem will always be even. Insights like these will greatly improve students' abilities to thoroughly complete this activity.

Management
1. You may wish to work on this problem over the course of several days so that groups have a chance to adequately explore the possibilities.
2. With the exception of the initial solution-discovery experience, this activity is meant to be done in groups.

Procedure
1. Give students the first student page and allow them to find one or two solutions individually, purely by trial and error. Inform students that they may carry over, but if they do, the number carried does not count as one of their digits, e.g., if a one is carried, ones may still be a part of the problem.
2. After all students have found at least one solution, hand out the second student page and have students get into groups so that they can discuss the questions and work together to find all of the possible solutions.
3. Before moving on to the second problem, have a time of class discussion where groups share their solutions and compare the total number discovered. The first problem (one + one = two) has a total of 16 unique solutions, but students should

not be given this information. Rather, challenge groups to determine the total number of solutions and justify this number in some way.

4. If groups have different numbers, try to determine the total number of solutions possible as a class. Go over the exploration questions, and encourage students to share any patterns they discovered.

5. Repeat this process with the second problem.

Connecting Learning

Problem One

1. Is O odd or even? Why? [O must always be even because the sum of any number added to itself is always even (E + E = O).]

2. What is the largest number that O could possibly be? [Four. O plus O is a one-digit number (T). If O were greater than four, the sum would be two digits.] ...the smallest? [Two. O must be greater than zero, because it is the first digit in the addends. As we have already shown, O must be even and four or less. This means that two is the smallest (and only other) possible value for O.] Why?

3. What is the largest number that T could possibly be? [Nine, because nine is the largest one-digit number.] ...the smallest? [Four, because T is the sum of O plus O, and the smallest number O can be is two.] Why?

4. What are the possible numbers that E could be? Justify your response. [The only possible values for E are one, two, six and seven. E cannot be three because 3 + 3 = 6 (E + E = O), and O cannot be greater than four. E cannot be four, eight, or nine for the same reason. E cannot be five because O cannot be zero.]

5. What patterns did you discover in your solutions? Based on these patterns, do you think you found all of the solutions that are possible? Why or why not?

Problem Two

1. What is the largest number T can be? Why? [Three, because nine is the largest one-digit number, and 3 + 3 + 3 = 9.]

2. Is it ever possible for O to be five? Why or why not? [No; 5 + 5 + 5 = 15. The five cannot be used as both the O and the X.]

3. Is it ever possible for X to be five? Why or why not? [No; the only way for X to be five is if O is five, which is impossible.]

4. Which letters can be zero? Why? [T and S cannot be zero because they are in the hundreds place. O and X cannot be zero because they are the ones place, and 0 + 0 + 0 = 0. W can be zero because it in the tens place and digits can carry from the ones place to make the value of I something other than zero. I can be zero because it is possible to have three numbers that sum to either 10 or 20 when one digit is carried from the ones place.]

Extension

Challenge students to develop their own cryptogram puzzles that have at least three different solutions. These puzzles need not be addition, but can be subtraction, multiplication, or even division.

Solutions

Problem One

There are 16 possible solutions for the first problem. The smallest possible sum is 412, and the largest possible sum is 964. The smallest possible addend is 206, and the largest possible addend is 482.

```
  ONE
+ ONE
  TWO
```

```
  206    216    231    236    271    281    286    291
+ 206  + 216  + 231  + 236  + 271  + 281  + 286  + 291
  412    432    462    472    542    562    572    582
```

```
  407    417    427    432    452    457    467    482
+ 407  + 417  + 427  + 432  + 452  + 457  + 467  + 482
  814    834    854    864    904    914    934    964
```

Letter	Possible Values
O	2, 4
N	0, 1, 2, 3, 5, 6, 7, 8, 9
E	1, 2, 6, 7
T	4, 5, 8, 9
W	0, 1, 3, 4, 5, 6, 7, 8

Patterns in Problem One

- All of the sums that are less than 800 end with two. All of the sums that are greater than 800 end with four.

- All of the addends that are less than 400 end with either one or six. All of the addends that are greater than 400 end with either two or seven.

- There are four solutions in the 400s, four solutions in the 500s, four solutions in the 800s, and four solutions in the 900s.

Problem Two

There are 35 possible solutions for the second problem. The smallest possible sum is 324, and the largest possible sum is 981. The smallest possible addend is 108, and the largest possible addend is 327.

```
  TWO
  TWO
+ TWO
  SIX
```

108	109	124	126	129	136	163
108	109	124	126	129	136	163
+ 108	+ 109	+ 124	+ 126	+ 129	+ 136	+ 163
324	327	372	378	387	408	489

168	169	176	178	182	183	189
168	169	176	178	182	183	189
+ 168	+ 169	+ 176	+ 178	+ 182	+ 183	+ 189
504	507	528	534	546	549	567

192	194	218	219	236	238	246
192	194	218	219	236	238	246
+ 192	+ 194	+ 218	+ 219	+ 236	+ 238	+ 246
576	582	654	657	708	714	738

261	263	267	269	273	291	304
261	263	267	269	273	291	304
+ 261	+ 263	+ 267	+ 269	+ 273	+ 291	+ 304
783	789	801	807	819	873	912

306	307	308	316	318	326	327
306	307	308	316	318	326	327
+ 306	+ 307	+ 308	+ 316	+ 318	+ 326	+ 327
918	921	924	948	954	978	981

Letter	Possible Values
T	1, 2, 3
W	0, 1, 2, 3, 4, 6, 7, 8, 9
O	1, 2, 3, 4, 6, 7, 8, 9
S	3, 4, 5, 6, 7, 8, 9
I	0, 1, 2, 3, 4, 5, 6, 7, 8
X	1, 2, 3, 4, 6, 7, 8, 9

*   Reprinted with permission from *Principles and Standards for School Mathematics*, 2000 by the National Council of Teachers of Mathematics. All rights reserved.

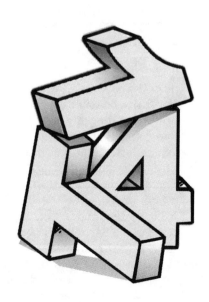

C	R	Y	P	T	I	C	A	L	L	Y
3	18	25	16	20	9	3	1	12	12	25

C	H	A	L	L	E	N	G	E	D
3	8	1	12	12	5	14	7	5	4

Key Question

How can you substitute a number for each letter in the problems so that the resulting addition problem is true?

Learning Goal

Students will:

solve simple cryptograms by replacing letters with the digits zero through nine so that the resulting addition problems are true.

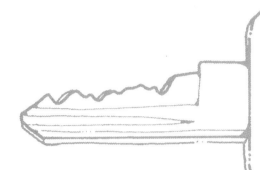

In the problem below, each letter stands for a different number between zero and nine. Assign a number to each letter so that the addition problem is correct. One solution has been given to get you started, there are several more. Record each solution you discover in the space provided. (The first digit must be greater than zero.)

$$
\begin{array}{r}
\textbf{ONE} \\
+\ \textbf{ONE} \\
\hline
\textbf{TWO}
\end{array}
\qquad
\begin{array}{r}
236 \\
+\ 236 \\
\hline
472
\end{array}
$$

C	R	Y	P	T	I	C	A	L	L	Y		C	H	A	L	L	E	N	G	E	D
3	18	25	16	20	9	3	1	12	12	25		3	8	1	12	12	5	14	7	5	4

Now that you have found at least one solution, use the questions below to help you think more logically about the problem. Once you have answered the questions, see how many more solutions you can find.

1. Is O odd or even? Why?

2. What is the largest number that O could possibly be? ...the smallest? Why?

3. What is the largest number that T could possibly be? ...the smallest? Why?

4. What are the possible numbers that E could be? Justify your response.

5. As you discover more solutions, record each possible value for the letters in the table below.

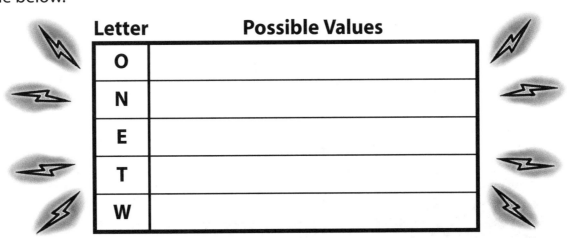

Letter	Possible Values
O	
N	
E	
T	
W	

6. What patterns do you see in the table and in your solutions? Based on these patterns, do you think you have found all of the solutions that are possible? Why or why not?

C	R	Y	P	T	I	C	A	L	L	Y		C	H	A	L	L	E	N	G	E	D
3	18	25	16	20	9	3	1	12	12	25		3	8	1	12	12	5	14	7	5	4

The challenge in this problem is the same as in the previous problem, but there are many more solutions. See how many you can find, and record them on a separate sheet of paper.

$$\begin{array}{r} \text{TWO} \\ \text{TWO} \\ +\text{TWO} \\ \hline \text{SIX} \end{array}$$

Answer these questions and complete the table to help you as you look for solutions.

1. What is the largest number T can be? Why?

2. Is it ever possible for O to be 5? Why or why not?

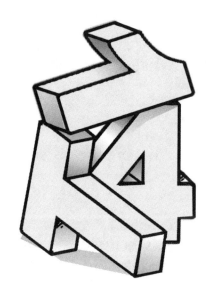

3. Is it ever possible for X to be 5? Why or why not?

4. Which letters could be zero? Why?

Letter	Possible Values
T	
W	
O	
S	
I	
X	

C	R	Y	P	T	I	C	A	L	L	Y
3	18	25	16	20	9	3	1	12	12	25

C	H	A	L	L	E	N	G	E	D
3	8	1	12	12	5	14	7	5	4

Connecting Learning

1. Is O odd or even? Why?

2. What is the largest number that O could possibly be? ...the smallest? Why?

3. What is the largest number that T could possibly be? ...the smallest? Why?

4. What are the possible numbers that E could be? Justify your response.

5. What patterns did you discover in your solutions? Based on these patterns, do you think you found all of the solutions that are possible? Why or why not?

Problem-Solving Strategies
Use Manipulatives

Sometimes it is helpful to use objects when solving a problem. These objects can represent the parts of the problem. Seeing the parts can help you understand how to find the answer. Anything can be a manipulative. You can use paper clips, pattern blocks, Unifix cubes, or even pieces of paper.

Topic
Problem solving

Key Question
How can you use your problem-solving skills to solve the different domino dilemmas?

Learning Goals
Students will:
1. divide sets of four dominoes into three sections so that each section has the same number of dots,
2. determine which shapes came from which dominoes, and
3. identify the domino from a set that is not shown in a picture.

Guiding Document
*NCTM Standards 2000**
- *Investigate, describe, and reason about the results of subdividing, combining, and transforming shapes*
- *Build new mathematical knowledge through problem solving*
- *Solve problems that arise in mathematics and in other contexts*
- *Apply and adapt a variety of appropriate strategies to solve problems*

Math
Geometry
 spatial sense
Logical thinking
Problem solving

Integrated Processes
Observing
Comparing and contrasting
Recording

Problem-Solving Strategies
Use manipulatives
Use logical thinking

Materials
Bamboo skewers or similar items
 (see *Management 1)*
Transparency film
Scissors
Student pages

Background Information
This activity was inspired by a similar series of puzzles in the March 2006 issue of the *Games* magazine that used playing cards. By changing from playing cards to dominoes and adding the use of manipulatives, the problems become appropriate for elementary students. In each case, the problems can be solved mentally, without the use of manipulatives. However, this is much more challenging, so the use of manipulatives is recommended.

Management
1. For the first challenge, students will need something that they can use to represent straight lines. A thin bamboo skewer cut in half will work, as will straightened jumbo paper clips or coffee stirrers.
2. Copy the extra page of small pieces for the second challenge onto transparency film. Give each student one set of pieces. They can lay these pieces on top of the page to check their solutions.
3. For the third challenge, each student will need a set of the 14 dominoes included. You may wish to copy these onto card stock to make them easier to handle.

Procedure
1. Distribute the first student page and skewers (or other items) to students. Go over the instructions and be sure that everyone is clear on the challenge.
2. Allow time for students to discover and record their solutions.
3. When students are finished, distribute the page for *Challenge Two* and one set of 14 dominoes to each student.
4. Have students cut out the set of 14 dominoes and use them to try and recreate the piles and determine which domino is upside down.
5. Give students the third challenge page and a set of small pieces on transparency film. Explain that they can cut out these pieces and use them to confirm their solutions. A piece must match up exactly with the domino beneath it.
6. Allow students to discover and record their solutions before closing with a time of class discussion and sharing.

Connecting Learning

1. What solutions did you find for *Challenge One?*
2. Are there multiple solutions for any of the problems? How do you know?
3. How did having the skewers help you solve the problem?
4. How did you solve *Challenge Two?* Did you need the paper dominoes? Why or why not?
5. Which domino did shape *a* come from? ...shape *b?* ...shape *c?* ...etc.
6. What was hard about this challenge? How did having the transparency shapes help?

Extension

Have students create their own challenges like those in parts one and two. Allow them to trade these with classmates to see if they can be solved.

Solutions

Challenge One

One possible solution is shown for each problem. There may be others.

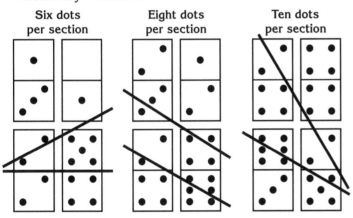

Challenge Two

In the first pile, the domino facedown is the six-five. In the second pile, the domino facedown is the five-two.

Challenge Three

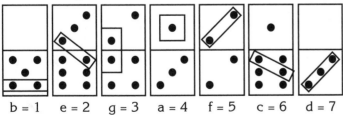

b = 1   e = 2   g = 3   a = 4   f = 5   c = 6   d = 7

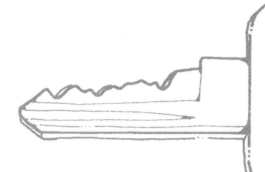

Domino Dilemmas

Learning Goals

Students will:

1. divide sets of four dominoes into three sections so that each section has the same number of dots,

2. determine which shapes came from which dominoes, and

3. identify the domino from a set that is not shown in a picture.

Domino Dilemmas

Draw two straight lines through each set of dominoes. Do this so that each of the three sections has the specified number of dots. In the example, one line is used to divide two dominoes so that the two sections each have five dots. Use your manipulatives to help look for solutions before you draw them on the paper.

Example: Five dots per section

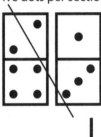

Six dots per section

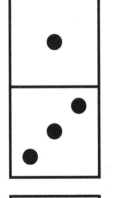 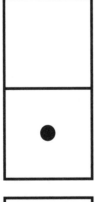

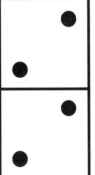 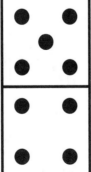

Eight dots per section

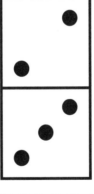 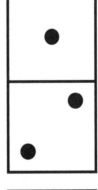

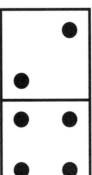 

Ten dots per section

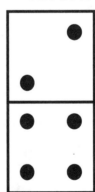 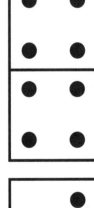

 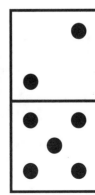

Domino Dilemmas

The pile shown here has all of the dominoes with a six. Figure out which domino is facedown. Circle that domino below.

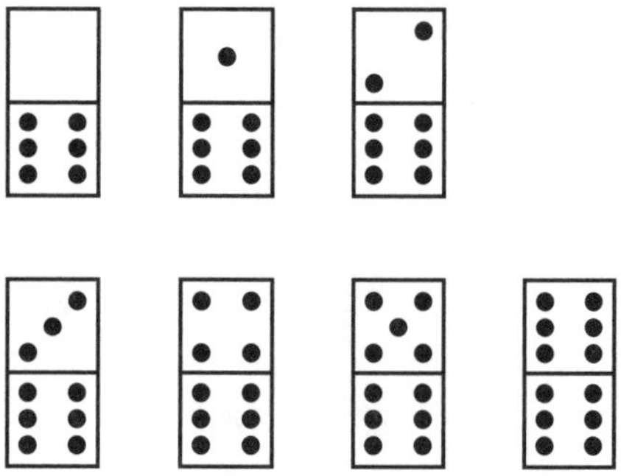

The pile shown here has all of the dominoes with a five. Figure out which domino is facedown. Circle that domino below.

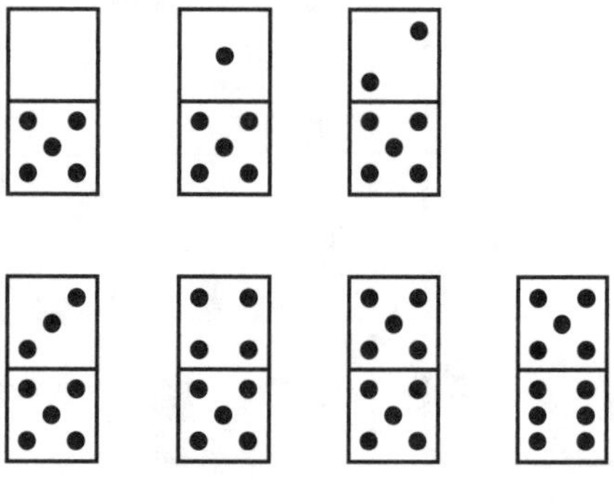

Domino Dilemmas

Copy this page onto card stock. Make enough copies for each student to have one set of dominoes.

Domino Dilemmas

Each of the shapes at the bottom of the page came from one of the dominoes pictured. The example shows a shape that came from the four-blank domino. Find the possible shapes for each domino. Use your transparencies to help you. Write the possibilities in the table. Use a process of elimination to find the solutions. Check your solutions using the transparencies.

Dominoes

Domino	Possible Shapes
1	
2	
3	
4	
5	
6	
7	

1.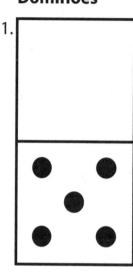

2.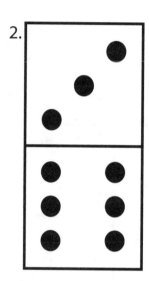

3.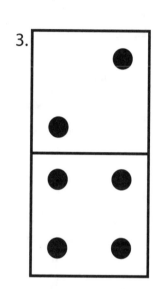

4.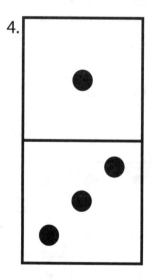

5.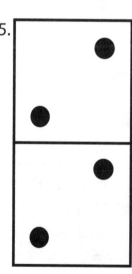

6.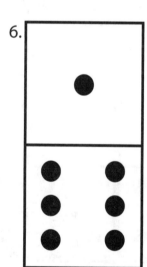

7.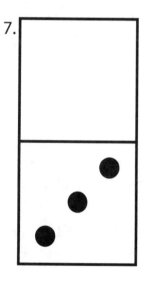

Shapes

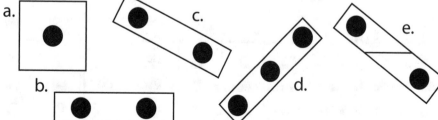

a.

b.

c.

d.

e.

f.

g.

Domino Dilemmas

Copy this page onto transparency film. Make enough copies for each student to have one set of shapes.

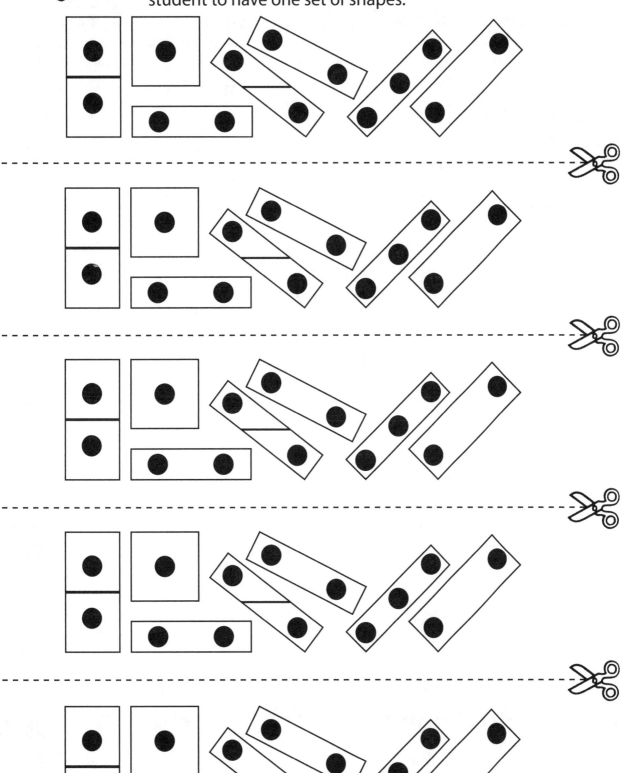

Connecting Learning

1. What solutions did you find for *Challenge One?*

2. Are there multiple solutions for any of the problems? How do you know?

3. How did having the skewers help you solve the problem?

4. How did you solve *Challenge Two?* Did you need the paper dominoes? Why or why not?

5. Which domino did shape *a* come from? ...shape *b?* ...shape *c?* ...etc.

6. What was hard about this challenge? How did having the transparency shapes help?

'Picks, Polygons, & Perimeters

Topic
Perimeter and area

Key Questions
1. What are all the possible shapes you can make using 12 toothpicks that have an area of five square units?
2. What are all the other possible areas of shapes that can be made using 12 toothpicks?

Learning Goals
Students will:
1. use 12 toothpicks to form the perimeters of polygons that enclose areas of five square units,
2. form the perimeters of polygons that enclose areas other than five square units,
3. find all the possible areas that can be enclosed by 12 toothpicks, and
4. look for patterns in their data.

Guiding Documents
Project 2061 Benchmarks
- *Mathematics is the study of many kinds of patterns, including numbers and shapes and operations on them. Sometimes patterns are studied because they help to explain how the world works or how to solve practical problems, sometimes because they are interesting in themselves.*
- *Length can be thought of as unit lengths joined together, area as a collection of unit squares, and volume as a set of unit cubes.*

NCTM Standards 2000*
- *Explore what happens to measurements of a two-dimensional shape such as its perimeter and area when the shape is changed in some way*
- *Describe, extend, and make generalizations about geometric and numeric patterns*
- *Build new mathematical knowledge through problem solving*

Math
Geometry
    perimeter
    area
Pattern recognition
Problem solving

Integrated Processes
Observing
Comparing and contrasting

Recording
Analyzing

Problem-Solving Strategies
Use manipulatives
Look for patterns
Organize the information

Materials
Flat toothpicks
Student pages

Background Information
Many years ago, when smoking was widespread and more socially acceptable, and cigarette lighters had not yet been invented, most people carried matches. During this time, match puzzles were quite common and popular. In fact, many people had a personal repertoire of five to 10 such puzzles that they used to challenge friends and acquaintances. This activity is one inspired by the classic match puzzles of old.

'Picks, Polygons, & Perimeters asks students to use 12 toothpicks to form the perimeters of shapes that enclose areas of five square units. The toothpicks can only be placed horizontally or vertically, and they cannot stick out or overlap. Each of the solutions is a polygon, although students may not recognize them as such. They are then challenged to find the other possible areas that can be enclosed with 12 toothpicks and to look for patterns in their solutions.

Management
1. Students should be encouraged to work collaboratively on this activity. When one person finds a solution, it should be shared with the others in the group and then each group member should make an individual record of the solution.
2. Solutions can be recorded by sketching them or by using the dot paper included with this activity.
3. *Part Two* of this activity can be done using an open-ended approach by giving students just the first page and the dot paper. For those students who need a bit more structure, a second page, which lists some questions to guide their thinking, is included.

Procedure
1. Divide students into groups and distribute the student page for *Part One*. If desired, provide the dot paper for sketching solutions.

91

2. Allow groups time to find and record all of the possible solutions.

3. Discuss what groups discovered and be sure that everyone has found all of the possibilities.

4. Distribute the page (or pages) for *Part Two* and allow groups time to make and record more discoveries.

5. Once groups have had time to analyze their solutions and look for patterns, discuss what they have discovered.

6. If desired, make a class list showing all of the solutions for each possible area and record some of the patterns discovered.

7. Allow students to explore some of the extensions and report their findings.

Connecting Learning

1. How many shapes were you able to find that have an area of five square units?

2. Do you think you have found them all? Why or why not?

3. What is the largest area that can be enclosed by 12 toothpicks? [nine square units] How do you know?

4. What is the smallest area that can be enclosed by 12 toothpicks? [five square units] Explain why this is so.

5. What are the other possible areas? [eight, seven, and six square units] How many solutions were you able to find for each area?

6. What patterns did you see in these numbers?

7. For any given area, what is the range of the number of sides of the polygons that produce this area? What patterns do you see in this data?

8. What other extensions did you think of to explore? What were your findings?

Extensions

1. Look at the number of areas possible using 10 toothpicks and 14 toothpicks, then compare this with what was found for 12 toothpicks.

2. Think through why odd numbers of toothpicks can't be used in this activity in its present form (with polygons limited to right angle corners).

3. Explore some of the patterns discovered. For example, an interesting pattern emerges when the number of sides the various polygons has for a given area is recorded. (Polygons with an area of five and a perimeter of 12 can have 4, 6, 8, 10, or 12 sides.)

4. Look at the number of toothpicks that would be needed in the interior of the polygons to delineate the internal squares: the square with an area of nine would need 12 such toothpicks, the polygons with an area of eight would need 10, the ones with an area of seven would need eight, and so on.

5. Make polygons with angles other than 90 degrees. For example, the 12 toothpicks can be used to

make a 3-4-5 right triangle with an area of six square units. Parallelograms and other polygons with areas of four, three, two, and one square units can also be made by allowing corners that are not right angles.

Solutions

Part One

There are 11 polygons that have an area of five square units. In this activity, rotations and reflections of an arrangement are all considered to be the same solution.

Area: Five square units

Part Two

The other possible areas are nine, eight, seven, and six square units. There is one shape with an area of nine square units, two shapes with an area of eight square units, four shapes with an area of seven square units, and seven shapes with an area of six square units. An area of four square units is not possible if the toothpicks must be arranged horizontally and vertically, but is possible if angles other than right angles are allowed (see *Extension 5*).

Area: Nine square units

Area: Eight square units

Area: Seven square units

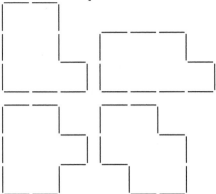

Area: Six square units

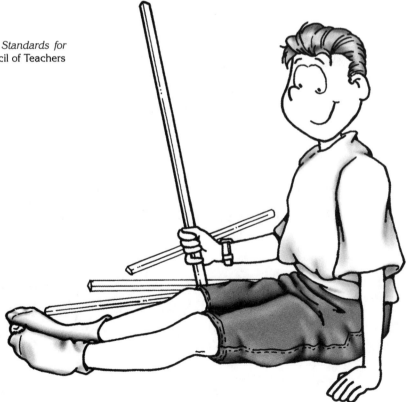

'Picks, Polygons, & Perimeters

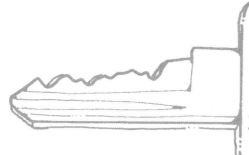

Key Questions

1. What are all the possible shapes you can make using 12 toothpicks that have an area of five square units?
2. What are all the other possible areas of shapes that can be made using 12 toothpicks?

Learning Goals

Students will:

1. use 12 toothpicks to form the perimeters of polygons that enclose areas of five square units,
2. form the perimeters of polygons that enclose areas other than five square units,
3. find all the possible areas that can be enclosed by 12 toothpicks, and
4. look for patterns in their data.

'Picks, Polygons, & Perimeters Part One

In this problem, you will use 12 toothpicks to make shapes with areas of five square units.

The toothpicks will form the perimeters of these polygons. The toothpicks can only be placed horizontally or vertically around the edges of the polygons. They cannot stick out or overlap. One possible solution is shown below.

Work with your group to find every possible solution. Draw your solutions below or record them on the dot paper.

Do you have all the possible solutions?
How do you know?

'Picks, Polygons, & Perimeters Part Two

In *Part One*, you found all of the polygons that have perimeters of 12 toothpicks and areas of five square units. The task in *Part Two* is to find all of the polygons, of any area, that can be made with 12 toothpicks. You must follow the same rules as in *Part One*. Toothpicks can only be placed horizontally or vertically. They cannot overlap or stick out.

As you work on this problem, you will need to make a record of your polygons. This can be done by sketching them or making a record on dot paper.

Once you have found all the possible areas and polygons, study this data. Record any patterns and/or mathematical discoveries you make.

'Picks, Polygons, & Perimeters Part Two

The following questions may help guide your thinking once you have collected your data.

What is the largest possible area possible? How do you know?

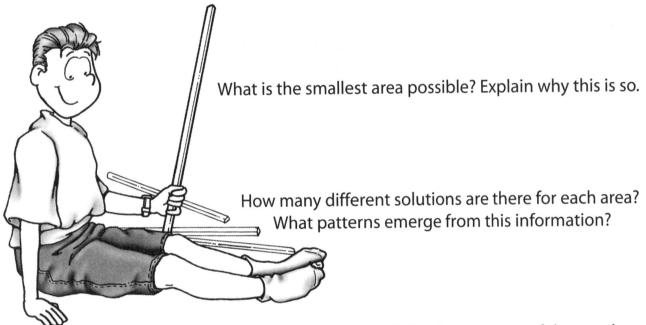

What is the smallest area possible? Explain why this is so.

How many different solutions are there for each area? What patterns emerge from this information?

Study all the polygons for any given area. What is the range of the number of sides of the polygons that produce this area? What patterns do see in this data?

If you were to use additional toothpicks to show the squares in the interiors of your polygons, how many extra would you need for each possible area? What pattern emerges from this data?

Think of some other questions or extensions for this activity and write them on the back of this paper. Pick one of these to explore further.

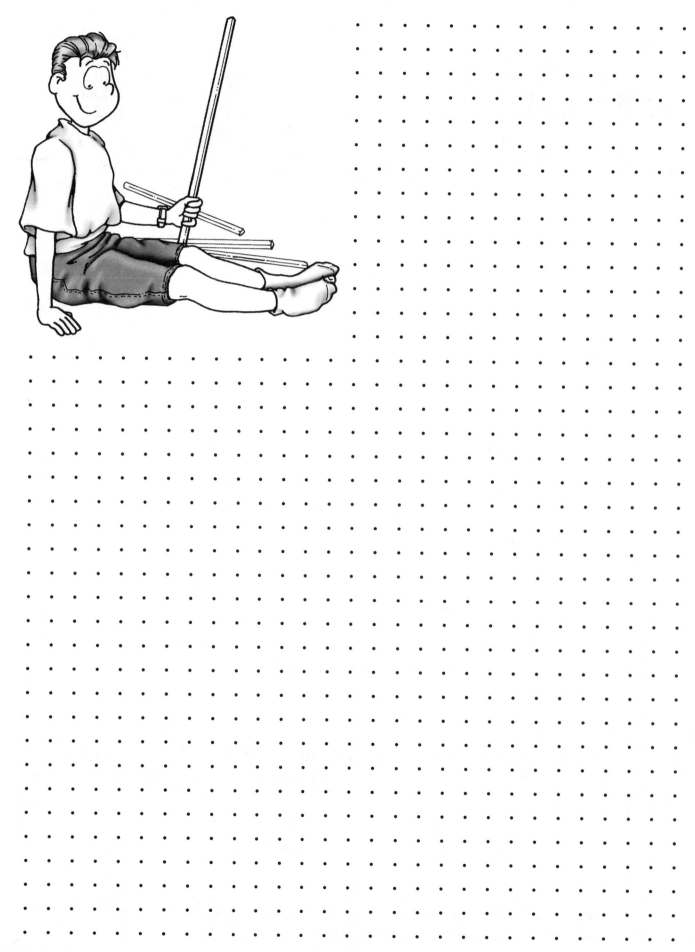

'Picks, Polygons, & Perimeters

Connecting Learning

1. How many shapes were you able to find that have an area of five square units?

2. Do you think you have found them all? Why or why not?

3. What is the largest area that can be enclosed by 12 toothpicks? How do you know?

4. What is the smallest area that can be enclosed by 12 toothpicks? Explain why this is so.

5. What are the other possible areas? How many solutions were you able to find for each area?

6. What patterns did you see in these numbers?

7. For any given area, what is the range of the number of sides of the polygons that produce this area? What patterns do you see in this data?

8. What other extensions did you think of to explore? What were your findings?

Pondering Partitions

Topic
Partitions

Key Question
What are the partition numbers for sets of one to seven objects?

Learning Goal
Students will find all of the ways to divide (partition) sets of one to seven objects when the order of the grouping does not matter.

Guiding Document
NCTM Standards 2000*

- *Build new mathematical knowledge through problem solving*
- *Solve problems that arise in mathematics and in other contexts*
- *Apply and adapt a variety of appropriate strategies to solve problems*
- *Monitor and reflect on the process of mathematical problem solving*

Math
Partitioning
Problem solving

Integrated Processes
Observing
Comparing and contrasting
Collecting and recording data
Organizing data

Problem-Solving Strategies
Use manipulatives
Organize the information

Materials
Beans (see *Management 3*)
Student pages

Background Information
This activity deals with the mathematical concept of partitioning. While this concept has a formal definition in set theory,** here we are simply looking at it as *grouping* the elements of a set in as many different ways as possible where order doesn't make a difference. To illustrate, study the following diagram, which partitions four beans in all the possible ways, according to the above definition.

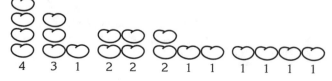

Mathematically, the *partition number, p(n)* for the set of four beans is five since the four beans can be divided into groups in five distinct ways. One way to record the partitions is to list each of the groupings using numbers as follows: 4, 31, 22, 211, 1111. (It is important to note that 31 indicates a group of three and a group of one, not thirty-one.) Since this recording method might be confusing to some students, another way to list the partitions would be to use number sentences as follows: 4, 3 + 1, 2 + 2, 2 + 1 + 1, and 1 + 1 + 1 + 1. Whichever recording method is used, it is easy to see that the partition number for four is five, or stated mathematically, $p(4) = 5$.

In this activity, students are challenged to find the partition number for sets of one to seven objects. While this might seem, at first glance, like a simple task involving nothing more than the manipulation of objects, it is far from trivial. As students will discover, it is not an easy task to find all the partitions for numbers greater than five, even when using manipulatives. In addition, this task demands some organizational scheme. Thus, this seemingly simple activity is a rich environment for problem solving. (This may explain why many mathematicians over the years, most notably Euler, Ramanujan, and Hardy, have spent a great deal of time studying partitioning.)

** A *partition* of set A is a collection of all the nonempty, pairwise disjoint subsets of A whose union is A.

Management
1. This activity can be done using either an open-ended or a structured approach. As an open-ended experience, give students only the first page, which introduces the problem and lets students come up with their own methods of doing the problem and recording their findings. For a more structured approach, give students the next two pages as well. These pages help students organize their data in a systematic way and suggests using number sentences as a recording scheme.
2. Students should be encouraged to work collaboratively in small groups.
3. Each student will need seven beans or other small manipulatives with which to work.

Procedure
1. Distribute the beans and the appropriate student page(s).
2. Have students get into groups and go over the instructions.

3. Allow time for groups to work through the problem and develop methods for recording their solutions.
4. Have groups share about the processes they went through to find the solutions.
5. If desired, explore some extensions that students develop.

Connecting Learning
1. How many partitions are there for two beans? ...three beans? ...four? ...etc.?
2. How do you know that you have found them all?
3. What methods did your group use for organizing your solutions?
4. How did organizing your solutions help?

Extensions
1. Explore partitions of numbers greater than seven. (The second and third student pages provide spaces for this in their tables.)
2. Look at what happens to the number of partitions if order does matter.

Solutions
A complete table with all the partitions for the numbers one through eight appears below. The recording scheme is the one described in the *Background Information*. Please note, however, that there are several other equally valid ways to record partitions. Even when using this particular method, the partitions could be listed in a different order. For example, when listing the partitions for six, all the partitions using two groups could go together (51, 42, 33) and then all the partitions with three groups (411, 321, 222) and then four groups, etc.

Number in set	Number of partitions using 1, 2, 3, ... groups									
	1	2	3	4	5	6	7			
1	1									
2	1	1								
3	1	1	1							
4	1	2	1	1						
5	1	2	2	1	1					
6	1	3	3	2	1	1				
7	1	3	4	3	2	1	1			

If your students want to extend the problem to find the partitions for eight and above, they will need quite a bit of room, as you can see from the answers provided. Nine has 30 partitions and 10 has 42 partitions. While it might seem that there should be a simple formula to find the number of partitions for any given set of objects, this is not the case. In fact, it took some of the top mathematicians of the twentieth century to come up with the exact formula. Unfortunately, this formula is so complicated that it is more appropriately studied at the university level.

Student Page Three

n	p(n)	Partitions
1	1	1
2	2	2, 11
3	3	3, 21, 111
4	5	4, 31, 22, 211, 1111
5	7	5, 41, 32, 311, 221, 2111, 11111
6	11	6, 51, 42, 411, 33, 321, 3111, 222, 2211, 21111, 111111
7	15	7, 61, 52, 511, 43, 421, 4111, 331, 322, 3211, 31111, 2221, 22111, 211111, 1111111
8	22	8, 71, 62, 611, 53, 521, 5111, 44, 431, 422, 4211, 41111, 332, 3311, 3221, 32111, 311111, 2222, 22211, 221111, 2111111, 11111111

Pondering Partitions

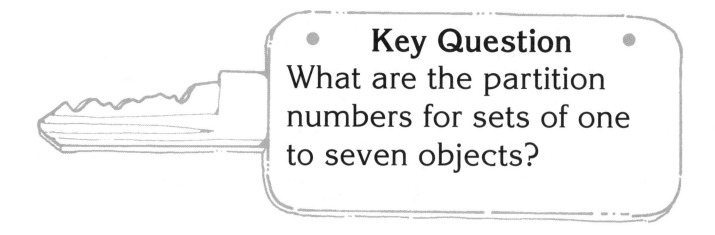

Key Question
What are the partition numbers for sets of one to seven objects?

Learning Goal

Students will:

find all of the ways to divide (partition) sets of one to seven objects when the order of the grouping does not matter.

Pondering Partitions

Study the figure below. It shows all the ways that four beans can be placed into groups where order does not matter. In mathematics, this grouping process is called **partitioning** and is of great interest to mathematicians. You may discover why as you work on this problem.

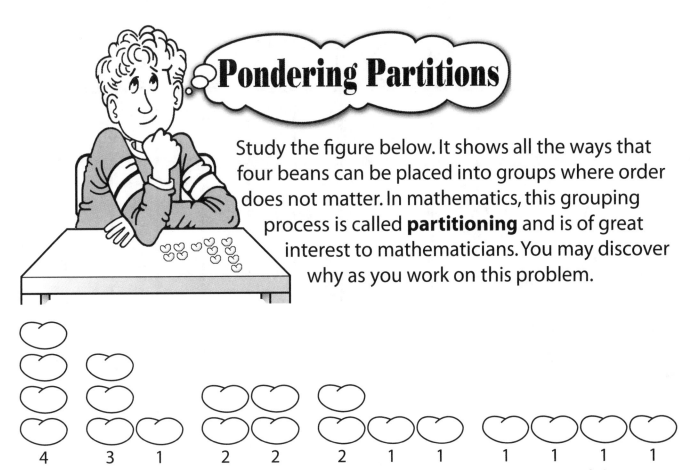

| 4 | 3 1 | 2 2 | 2 1 1 | 1 1 1 1 |

As you can see, four beans can be partitioned in five distinct ways if the order of the groups does not matter. Your challenge in this activity is to find **all** the partitions for sets of one to seven objects. You will need to find a way to record the partitions for each set. Please show your work as you explore this problem.

Challenge: Think of some other related questions or extensions to explore.

Pondering Partitions

One way to record the partitions for a set of objects is to use number sentences. For four objects the number sentences showing the partitions would be 4, 3 + 1, 2 + 2, 2 + 1 + 1 and 1 + 1 + 1 + 1. Using this method, or another one that you invent, fill in the chart below.

Number	Partitions
1	
2	
3	
4	
5	
6	
7	

Pondering Partitions

Use the information from the previous page to complete the following chart.

Number in set	Number of partitions using 1, 2, 3, … groups									
	1	2	3	4	5	6	7			
1										
2										
3										
4										
5										
6										
7										

SOLVE IT! 5th

105

Pondering Partitions

Connecting Learning

1. How many partitions are there for two beans? …three beans? …four? …etc.?

2. How do you know that you have found them all?

3. What methods did your group use for organizing your solutions?

4. How did organzing your solutions help?

Problem-Solving Strategies
Draw out the Problem

Drawing pictures is a useful problem-solving tool. Pictures help you keep track of important information. They also help when a problem has lots of details. With a picture, you can see every part of the problem at once. Keep the pictures simple. You don't need to spend lots of time drawing.

DOUBLE PLAY

Topic
Data analysis

Key Question
How can you make sense of data that appear to describe an impossibility?

Learning Goal
Students will try to make sense of confusing data that involve overlapping sets.

Guiding Document
NCTM Standards 2000*
- *Create and use representations to organize, record, and communicate mathematical ideas*
- *Build new mathematical knowledge through problem solving*
- *Apply and adapt a variety of appropriate strategies to solve problems*
- *Compare different representations of the same data and evaluate how well each representation shows important aspects of the data*

Math
Data analysis
Logical thinking
Problem solving

Integrated Processes
Observing
Comparing and contrasting
Recording
Organizing
Interpreting

Problem-Solving Strategies
Draw out the problem
Organize the information
Use logical thinking

Materials
Student pages
Manipulatives, optional

Background Information
This problem comes from the mathematical field of set theory. Set theory is a relative newcomer in mathematics as its origins date back only one century. (Some of the more traditional branches of mathematics like arithmetic, algebra, and geometry date back thousands of years.) Set theory first entered the K-12 school mathematics curriculum during the New Math era of the 1960s. One of set theory's most visible symbols is the Venn diagram. This powerful mathematical tool was invented by the English mathematician, John Venn (born August 4, 1834).

Venn diagrams are especially useful when working with the overlapping data presented by intersecting sets. These types of data often cause problems for those trying to make sense of them. This occurs because the data in the overlap, or intersection, are counted as part of each intersecting set. An example of the confusion arising from this double counting appeared in the news some time ago when statisticians in California admitted that the numbers they had reported on children born out of wedlock were inaccurate. The statisticians had compiled data on the number of children born to unmarried parents by comparing fathers' and mothers' last names on birth certificates—those last names that were the same placed the child in one category and those that were different placed the child in another. Unfortunately, this particular method of collecting data placed children born to married women who kept their maiden names into the category of children born to parents who weren't married, thus artificially inflating the (reported) number of children born out of wedlock. The statisticians had assumed that they were dealing with two non-intersecting (disjoint) sets of data—married and unmarried parents—when in reality they were dealing with the intersecting sets shown in the Venn diagram here.

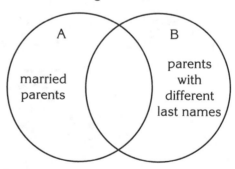

Management
1. Students should be encouraged to work on this problem collaboratively.
2. The big idea in this lesson is that data in intersecting sets have to be dealt with carefully because the items in the set intersection are counted more than once. Students immediately discover this

when they observe that the numbers given do not add up (14 + 4 + 15 = 33). Since the challenge is to make sense of these data, they will have to find a way to work with the numbers to produce the answer of 25. While using a Venn diagram is a powerful way to do this, it is not likely that students will think of this unless they have had lots of experience with them prior to this activity.

Procedure

1. Distribute the student page and have students get into groups.
2. Allow time for groups to work together to find a way to make sense of the data. Working with the numbers alone, students may realize that the four who play both soccer and baseball need to be subtracted from the total numbers who reported playing each sport (14 + 15 – 4 = 25). Students may also try such approaches as acting the problem out, making charts or tallies, or drawing pictures. In each approach, the overlap (four people playing both sports) must be accounted for.
3. Have groups share the methods they used for making sense of the data. Discuss the differences between the methods and how effective each seems to be.
4. The Venn diagram here shows perhaps the best way to present this information. If none of the groups comes up with this way of working with the data, it might be an appropriate time to introduce (or review) Venn diagrams.

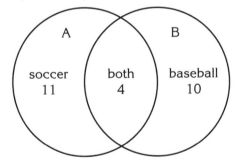

Connecting Learning

1. What appears to be wrong with the data when you first read them? [There are more responses than the total number of people surveyed.]
2. How can you make sense of the data? [show how the sets overlap]
3. What method did your group use to show how the data make sense?
4. How does this compare to methods used by other groups? Do you think one method works better than the others? Why or why not?

DOUBLE PLAY

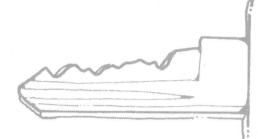

Key Question

How can you make sense of data that appear to describe an impossibility?

Learning Goal

Students will:

try to make sense of confusing data that involve overlapping sets.

DOUBLE PLAY

Twenty-five students were polled about their participation in after-school sports. Fifteen students reported playing soccer while 14 students said they participated in baseball. Four students said they played both soccer and baseball.

The above statements are all true. How is this possible?

Try to show or explain these data in a way that makes sense.

111

DOUBLE PLAY

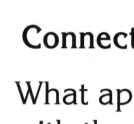

Connecting Learning

1. What appears to be wrong with the data when you first read them?

2. How can you make sense of the data?

3. What method did your group use to show how the data make sense?

4. How does this compare to methods used by other groups? Do you think one method works better than the others? Why or why not?

Gag Gifts Galore

Topic
Problem solving

Key Question
How many boxes will you need to make the gag gift?

Learning Goal
Students will solve a story problem using various problem-solving strategies.

Guiding Document
NCTM Standards 2000*
- *Apply and adapt a variety of appropriate strategies to solve problems*
- *Organize and consolidate their mathematical thinking through communication*
- *Communicate their mathematical thinking coherently and clearly to peers, teachers, and others*
- *Analyze and evaluate the mathematical thinking and strategies of others*
- *Use the language of mathematics to express mathematical ideas precisely*

Math
Problem solving

Integrated Processes
Observing
Collecting and recording data
Applying

Problem-Solving Strategies
Draw out the problem
Organize the information

Materials
Student page

Background Information
Story problems, like the one presented here, are often missed by students and adults alike. This happens because all too often, mathematical operations and procedures are applied without thinking. To solve this problem accurately, students need to make a list, draw a picture, or apply some other problem-solving strategy instead of just multiplying the numbers together. When an organized approach is used, it is obvious that there are 24 tiny boxes, six small boxes, two medium-sized boxes, and one large box for a total of 33 boxes.

Management
1. This activity can be done individually or by groups of students.
2. Much of the *learning* in this activity comes when students come up with several different answers and then try to reconcile the discrepancy. *Try to resist the temptation to jump in and solve the problem for the students.*
3. The sharing of answers and the discussion that follows are very important. Try to act as a facilitator in this process to help students.

Procedure
1. Distribute the student pages and ask students to work on the two problems posed.
2. After students have had time to come up with their answers, have several students share and describe how they came up with these answers.
3. Conduct a whole-class discussion on the findings of this activity.

Connecting Learning
1. How many boxes are needed altogether? [The gag gift requires 24 tiny boxes, six small boxes, two medium boxes, and one large box for a total of 33. (Some students may come up with an answer of 24 boxes since this is the product of the four numbers. Others might come up with an answer of 10 since this is the sum of the four numbers.)]
2. What problem-solving methods did you use to find the solution? [Various answers: drew pictures, made a list, constructed a table, etc.]
3. How many candies are needed? [Each of the tiny boxes has one candy, so 24 pieces are needed.]

* Reprinted with permission from *Principles and Standards for School Mathematics*, 2000 by the National Council of Teachers of Mathematics. All rights reserved.

Gag Gifts Galore

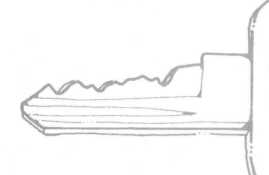

Key Question

How many boxes will you need to make the gag gift?

Learning Goal

Students will:

solve a story problem using various problem-solving strategies.

Gag Gifts Galore

This holiday season you decide to give your friend a gag gift that takes a long time to open. You have a large box into which you put two medium-sized boxes. You then put three small boxes into each of the medium-sized ones. Finally, you put four tiny boxes into each of the small boxes. Each of these tiny boxes contains a piece of candy.

Use this information to answer the following questions. Show your work and be ready to explain the problem-solving process you used.

Altogether, how many boxes do you need for this gag gift?

How many pieces of candy do you need?

Gag Gifts Galore

Connecting Learning

1. How many boxes are needed altogether?

2. What problem-solving methods did you use to find the solution?

3. How many candies are needed?

Santa's Ladder

Topic
Problem solving

Key Question
How many rungs are on Santa's ladder?

Learning Goal
Students will use problem-solving strategies to determine the number of rungs on a ladder based on descriptions of movements on that ladder.

Guiding Document
NCTM Standards 2000*
- *Build new mathematical knowledge through problem solving*
- *Solve problems that arise in mathematics and in other contexts*
- *Apply and adapt a variety of appropriate strategies to solve problems*
- *Monitor and reflect on the process of mathematical problem solving*

Math
Problem solving

Integrated Processes
Observing
Recording
Interpreting

Problem-Solving Strategy
Draw out the problem

Materials
Student page

Background Information
   Santa's Ladder is a multi-step story problem similar to the ones that appear in many mathematics textbooks. University educators often refer to these problems as translation problems since their solutions require translating back and forth between oral and written language, and mathematical or computational language. While these story, or translation, problems should not be the mainstay of a problem-solving diet, they do have a place in a well-balanced approach to problem solving.

Management
1. Have students work on the problem in groups. This approach should facilitate a good deal of mathematical communication as students clarify their thoughts and discuss their insights with others in their group while working on the problem together.
2. After introducing the problem, you may find that some groups need help. Avoid the temptation to solve the problem for the students by giving too much help. Often, a hint is all that is needed. For example, if a group is stuck at the beginning and just can't get started, you might ask, "What is the significance of knowing that the ladder has a middle rung?" This should get them started and lead them to discover that the answer will be an odd number and that there will be an equal number of rungs above and below the middle rung (both of which are important pieces of the problem).

Procedure
1. Have students get into groups and distribute the student page.
2. Read through the problem as a class and be sure everyone understands the challenge.
3. Allow time for the groups to work on the problem and develop a solution.
4. When the groups have come up with their answers, have them prepare a formal presentation for the rest of the class. This presentation should include sharing their approaches to the problem and the problem-solving processes they used, as well as their answers.

Connecting Learning
1. How many rungs are there on Santa's ladder? [17] How do you know?
2. What method did your group use to find the answer?
3. How does this compare to the methods used by other groups?
4. Do you think one method was more effective than the others? Why or why not?

*   Reprinted with permission from *Principles and Standards for School Mathematics*, 2000 by the National Council of Teachers of Mathematics. All rights reserved.

Santa's Ladder

Key Question

How many rungs are on Santa's ladder?

Learning Goal

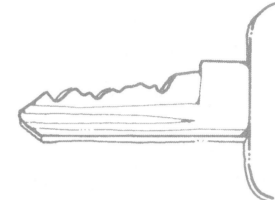

Students will:

use problem-solving strategies to determine the number of rungs on a ladder based on descriptions of movements on that ladder.

Santa's Ladder

Santa is standing on the middle rung of a ladder on his way up to the chimney. He climbs up three rungs, and then goes down five rungs. Finally, he climbs up 10 rungs to get to the top. How many rungs are there on the ladder?

Use the space below to show how you got your answer. Be prepared to share your answer and your problem-solving strategies with the class.

Connecting Learning

1. How many rungs are there on Santa's ladder? How do you know?

2. What method did your group use to find the answer?

3. How does this compare to the methods used by other groups?

4. Do you think one method was more effective than the others? Why or why not?

Problem-Solving Strategies
Organize the Information

It is often helpful to organize the information when trying to solve problems. You can put what you know into a list, chart, or table. Then you can see what you still need to solve the problem. You can also use this strategy when you need to find lots of different solutions.

Square Sections

Topic
Geometry

Key Questions
1. What shape combinations can you make by folding a square?
2. How can they be organized?
3. What patterns exist in the shape combinations?

Learning Goals
Students will:
1. search for every possible combination of shapes that can be created by folding a square with two straight lines,
2. develop a scheme for organizing those shape combinations, and
3. look for patterns within the shape combination possibilities.

Guiding Documents
Project 2061 Benchmark
- *Mathematics is the study of many kinds of patterns, including numbers and shapes and operations on them. Sometimes patterns are studied because they help to explain how the world works or how to solve practical problems, sometimes because they are interesting in themselves.*

NCTM Standards 2000*
- *Investigate, describe, and reason about the results of subdividing, combining, and transforming shapes*
- *Describe, extend, and make generalizations about geometric and numeric patterns*
- *Build new mathematical knowledge through problem solving*
- *Apply and adapt a variety of appropriate strategies to solve problems*

Math
Geometry
  2-D shapes
Pattern recognition
Problem solving

Integrated Processes
Observing
Comparing and contrasting
Collecting and recording data
Organizing data
Analyzing

Problem-Solving Strategies
Organize the information
Look for patterns
Use manipulatives

Materials
Colored paper squares (see *Management 1*)
Butcher paper or chart paper
Glue sticks
Student pages

Background Information
This activity is an open-ended task that challenges students to identify geometric shapes, discover multiple solutions, develop an organizational strategy, and look for patterns. The challenges are to discover every possible combination of shapes that can be created by folding a square with two straight lines, to develop a scheme for organizing those shape combinations, and to look for patterns within the shape combination possibilities.

Students will quickly discover that the ways in which you can divide a square with two straight lines are virtually limitless. However, there is a finite number of possible shape combinations. It is important for students to correctly and consistently identify the shape combinations so that they can determine whether solutions they discover are new combinations or merely different ways of creating the same shape combination.

Management
1. Students will need a large number of paper squares between seven and 10 centimeters in size. If you have access to an Ellison machine, cut squares out of colored paper using one of the square die cuts. Colored paper is recommended so that there will be a contrast between the squares and the butcher paper on which students will eventually be organizing their solutions. If you do not have access to an Ellison machine, you can use a paper cutter to create the squares. A third option is to use three-inch square sticky notes. Whichever method you choose, students should have as many squares as they need to explore the variety of solutions that are possible.
2. Students should work together in groups of three to five. Each group will be responsible for discovering as many different solutions as possible and creating a chart—based on the organizational scheme it develops—to display the solutions.

3. Each group will need a piece of butcher paper or chart paper on which to organize its solutions. The size of the paper needed will be determined by the size of paper squares used and the number of solutions discovered.

Procedure

1. Have students get into groups and distribute the first student page.

2. Go over the instructions and the geometric terms students will be using to identify the combinations in their squares: triangle, quadrilateral, square, rectangle, trapezoid, parallelogram, pentagon, and hexagon. Be sure that students are familiar with these shapes and how to recognize them before you begin. Note that in this activity, the term *quadrilateral* is used to describe all four-sided figures that do not belong to any of the more specific categories listed (square, rectangle, trapezoid, etc.).

3. Give each group a supply of squares and allow time for them to make discoveries.

4. When groups have discovered at least 15 different solutions, give students the second student page and a sheet of butcher or chart paper on which they can organize these solutions.

5. Encourage groups to come up with a logical scheme for organizing their squares and have them describe it on the student page.

6. Be sure that groups clearly label each grouping of squares (*Two Triangles, One Trapezoid,* etc.) and label the shapes that are contained within each square (*four squares, two triangles and one rectangle,* etc.). Here's a sample of how part of one group's chart might look:

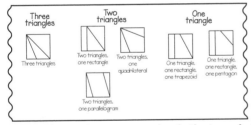

7. After students have organized their solutions, have them spend some time answering the questions on the third student page and thinking about the patterns that they see.

8. When students have completed the third student page, take some time as a class to compare the various solution charts and discuss organizing schemes.

Connecting Learning

1. How many different shape combinations was your group able to find?

2. Do you think you have found them all? Why or why not?

3. Which of your categories has the most solutions in it? Why do you think this is?

4. What is the greatest number of shapes possible when you divide a square using two folds? ...the fewest number possible? Why?

5. Is it ever possible to have a shape with more than six sides? Why or why not?

6. What other shapes are possible when one shape is a hexagon? ...a pentagon? ...a rectangle? Why?

7. What do your solutions say about shapes and how they are related?

8. Are there any patterns in the way shapes are combined?

9. How did your group organize your solutions? How does that compare to the methods used by other groups?

10. Is there one scheme that seems to be the most logical? Explain.

11. Were there solutions discovered by some groups that other groups did not discover?

Extensions

1. Create a whole-class chart that records all of the unique shape combinations discovered. See if you can discover every possible combination that can be made with two straight folds in a square.

2. Eliminate the rule that requires you to open the square before making your second fold. This allows for many more shape combinations than are possible using two straight folds.

3. Explore the results of folding other shapes like triangles, parallelograms, trapezoids, rectangles, and more.

Solutions

These solutions have been organized into five categories. One category is for folds that produce four shapes that are all the same type, though not necessarily congruent. The rest of the categories are grouped by the number of triangles in each solution, regardless of the other shapes present. There may be other solutions not shown here, and there are many other possible ways to organize the solutions.

Four shapes of the same type

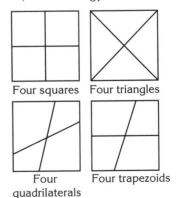

Three triangles

Three triangles

Three triangles, one quadrilateral

Three triangles, one pentagon

One triangle, one quadrilateral, one pentagon

One triangle, one trapezoid, one pentagon

One triangle, one rectangle, one trapezoid

Two triangles

Two triangles, one rectangle

Two triangles, one quadrilateral

Two triangles, one parallelogram

Two triangles, one trapezoid

One triangle, two quadrilaterals, one pentagon

One triangle, two trapezoids, one pentagon

Two triangles, one pentagon

Two triangles, one hexagon

Two triangles, two quadrilaterals

Two triangles, two trapezoids

No triangles

Two squares, two rectangles

Three rectangles

One rectangle, two trapezoids

Two triangles, two pentagons

Two triangles, one trapezoid, one pentagon

Two triangles, one quadrilateral, one pentagon

One parallelogram, two trapezoids

Three trapezoids

One triangle

One triangle, two trapezoids

One triangle, three trapezoids

One triangle, one rectangle, one pentagon

One triangle, one parallelogram, one trapezoid

One triangle, one quadrilateral, one trapezoid

Square Sections

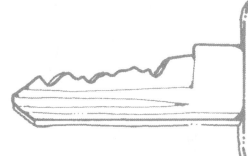

Key Questions

1. What shape combinations can you make by folding a square?
2. How can they be organized?
3. What patterns exist in the shape combinations?

Learning Goals

Students will:

1. search for every possible combination of shapes that can be created by folding a square with two straight lines,
2. develop a scheme for organizing those shape combinations, and
3. look for patterns within the shape combination possibilities.

Square Sections

Your challenge is to see how many different shape combinations you can discover by folding a square two times. For example, if you fold a square in half vertically and horizontally, it will result in four smaller squares.

There are two rules that govern the ways you may fold:

1. Each fold that you make must go all the way across the paper.
2. You must unfold the paper before you make the second fold.

Yes

No

Use the following terms to identify the shape combinations in your squares:

Triangle: Three sides
Quadrilateral: Four sides
Square: Four congruent sides, four right angles
Rectangle: Two sets of congruent sides, four right angles
Trapezoid: Quadrilateral with only one set of parallel sides
Parallelogram: Quadrilateral with two sets of parallel sides
Pentagon: Five sides
Hexagon: Six sides

There are many different ways to get the same shape combination. Focus your attention on getting different shape combinations. For example, although the folds below look different, they all result in the same shape combination: One triangle, two trapezoids.

Square
Sections

Folding Challenges

Find a way to fold:

- three triangles
- three rectangles
- three trapezoids
- two triangles and one rectangle
- one triangle and two trapezoids

What other shape combinations can you find?

Once your group has found at least 15 solutions, you will be ready to organize your findings. On your sheet of butcher paper, arrange your squares into logical groupings. You may make as many or as few groupings as you want. Make a heading for each grouping and glue each square in the appropriate place. Record the shape combinations in each solution by writing them below the squares.

Describe your group's plan for organizing your solutions.

Why did you choose this method of organizing your solutions?

Do you think this is the best way your solutions could be organized? Why or why not?

Square Sections

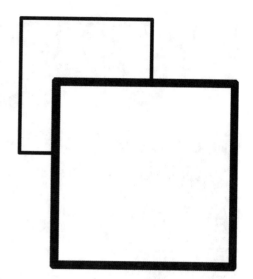

Once you have organized your solutions, answer the questions below. Use the back of your paper if necessary.

1. How many different shape combinations was your group able to find?

2. Do you think you have found them all? Why or why not?

3. Which of your categories has the most solutions in it? Why do you think this is?

4. What is the greatest number of shapes possible when you divide a square using two folds? …the fewest number possible? Why?

5. Is it ever possible to have a shape with more than six sides? Why or why not?

6. What other shapes are possible when one shape is a hexagon? …a pentagon? …a rectangle? Why?

7. What other patterns do you see in your solutions?

Connecting Learning

1. How many different shape combinations was your group able to find?

2. Do you think you have found them all? Why or why not?

3. Which of your categories has the most solutions in it? Why do you think this is?

4. What is the greatest number of shapes possible when you divide a square using two folds? ...the fewest number possible? Why?

5. Is it ever possible to have a shape with more than six sides? Why or why not?

6. What other shapes are possible when one shape is a hexagon? ...a pentagon? ...a rectangle? Why?

Square Sections

Connecting Learning

7. What do your solutions say about shapes and how they are related?

8. Are there any patterns in the way shapes are combined?

9. How did your group organize your solutions? How does that compare to the methods used by other groups?

10. Is there one scheme that seems to be the most logical? Explain.

11. Were there solutions discovered by some groups that other groups did not discover?

130

Counting Quadrilaterals

Topic
Problem solving

Key Question
How many quadrilaterals are there in the four by four grid?

Learning Goal
Students will determine the number of quadrilaterals in a four by four square grid.

Guiding Documents
Project 2061 Benchmark
- *Mathematics is the study of many kinds of patterns, including numbers and shapes and operations on them. Sometimes patterns are studied because they help to explain how the world works or how to solve practical problems, sometimes because they are interesting in themselves.*

NCTM Standards 2000*
- *Describe, extend, and make generalizations about geometric and numeric patterns*
- *Build new mathematical knowledge through problem solving*
- *Apply and adapt a variety of appropriate strategies to solve problems*

Math
Problem solving

Integrated Processes
Observing
Comparing and contrasting
Collecting and recording data
Organizing
Generalizing
Applying

Problem-Solving Strategies
Organize the information
Look for patterns

Materials
Scissors
Student pages

Background Information
This activity challenges students to find the total number of quadrilaterals (this includes both the squares and the rectangles) in a four by four square

grid. Careful organization of information is required, as students must be sure to count each quadrilateral only once while also being sure to count all of the possible sizes and shapes. If the data are carefully organized, patterns can be seen that allow students to generalize their results to square grids of other sizes.

Management
1. This activity can be presented as an open-ended exploration or as a more guided problem. If you want to use an open-ended approach, simply give students the first page and let them tackle the problem in any manner they choose. If you desire a more structured approach, give students the second page in addition to the first. The questions on the second page should help students grapple with the problem. If even more guidance is needed, give students all three pages.
2. Copy extra grids and let students cut out the different-sized quadrilaterals. This allows them to move the quadrilaterals around on the grid to more accurately determine how many of each size there are.

Connecting Learning
1. How many different-sized squares are in the grid? [4] What are they? [1 x 1, 2 x 2, 3 x 3, 4 x 4]
2. How many squares of each size are there? [1 x 1 = 16, 2 x 2 = 9, 3 x 3 = 4, 4 x 4 = 1] What patterns do you see in these numbers? [They are the first four square numbers.]
3. How many squares are there total? [30]
4. How many different-sized rectangles are in the grid? [12] What are they? [1 x 2, 2 x 1, 1 x 3, 3 x 1, 1 x 4, 4 x 1, 2 x 3, 3 x 2, 2 x 4, 4 x 2, 3 x 4, 4 x 3]
5. How many rectangles of each size are there? (See *Solutions*.) What patterns do you see in these numbers?
6. What is the total number of quadrilaterals in the grid? [100]
7. How many squares do you think would be in a 5 x 5 grid? ...rectangles? ...total quadrilaterals? Why?

Procedure
1. Distribute the student page(s) and allow time for students to work on the activity.
2. Have them share their solutions and the methods they used to reach those solutions.
3. Encourage students to explore some of the extensions and look for additional patterns in similar problems.

Extensions

1. Look at the number of quadrilaterals in smaller grids (one by one, two by two, and three by three) and see if there are any patterns in these numbers. Use the pattern to predict how many rectangles would be in larger grids.
2. Find a generalization, or *n*th term, for the series.
3. Organize the solutions as show in the square table and have students look for some of the patterns that can be seen.

Solutions

There are a total of 100 quadrilaterals in the grid. This table illustrates the break-down.

Squares	Number of Each
1 x 1	16
2 x 2	9
3 x 3	4
4 x 4	1
Horizontal Rectangles	
1 x 2	12
1 x 3	8
1 x 4	4
2 x 3	6
2 x 4	3
3 x 4	2
Vertical Rectangles	
2 x 1	12
3 x 1	8
4 x 1	4
3 x 2	6
4 x 2	3
4 x 3	2
Total Quadrilaterals	100

If the solutions are organized in a different way, some intersting patterns can be seen. Consider the table below.

1 x 1	2 x 1	3 x 1	4 x 1	Row Total
16	12	8	4	40
1 x 2	2 x 2	3 x 2	4 x 2	
12	9	6	3	30
1 x 3	2 x 3	3 x 3	4 x 3	
8	6	4	2	20
1 x 4	2 x 4	3 x 4	4 x 4	
4	3	2	1	10

Grand Total 100

Patterns

- The numbers in the first row and the first column go down by four as you move from left to right or top to bottom. In the second row and column they go down by three, in the third row and column they go down by two, and in the fourth row and column they go down by one.
- The sums of the numbers in the horizontal rows decrease by 10 as you move down the table. The same is true of the sums of the numbers in the vertical columns as you move from left to right.
- The numbers on the diagonal (top left to bottom right) are the first four square numbers.
- The top left to bottom right diagonal forms a line of symmetry in the table. Numbers in equivalent places on either side of the line are the same.

* Reprinted with permission from *Principles and Standards for School Mathematics*, 2000 by the National Council of Teachers of Mathematics. All rights reserved.

Counting Quadrilaterals

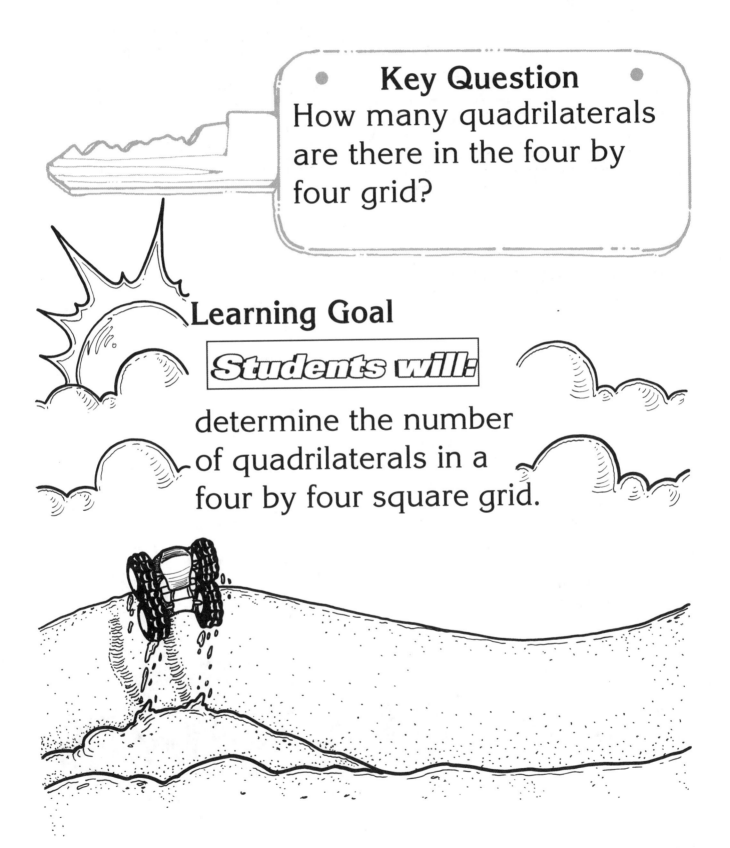

Key Question

How many quadrilaterals are there in the four by four grid?

Learning Goal

Students will:

determine the number of quadrilaterals in a four by four square grid.

133

Counting Quadrilaterals

How many quadrilaterals (four-sided figures) are in the 4 x 4 grid below?

Since quadrilaterals include squares and rectangles, remember to count both. Also, both horizontal (i.e., 2 x 3) and vertical (i.e., 3 x 2) rectangles should be counted.

Extension: How many quadrilaterals are in a 1 x 1, 2 x 2, or a 3 x 3 square grid? What about a 5 x 5 or a 6 x 6 square grid? Try to find a pattern in these numbers.

Counting Quadrilaterals

Answer the following questions about the grid on the first page. This will help you determine the total number of rectangles.

1. How many different-sized squares are in the grid? List each size below.

2. How many squares of each size are there? List them.

3. How many different horizontal rectangles are in the grid? List them.

4. How many horizontal rectangles of each size are there? List them.

5. How many different vertical rectangles are there? List them.

6. How many vertical rectangles of each size are there? List them.

7. Use the information above to find the total number of quadrilaterals in the grid.

Counting Quadrilaterals

How many quadrilaterals are in the 4 x 4 grid on the first page?
Fill in the table below to find the answer.

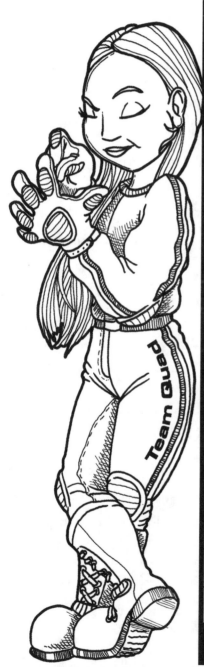

Squares	Number of Each
1 x 1	
2 x 2	
3 x 3	
4 x 4	
Horizontal Rectangles	
1 x 2	
1 x 3	
1 x 4	
2 x 3	
2 x 4	
3 x 4	
Vertical Rectangles	
2 x 1	
3 x 1	
4 x 1	
3 x 2	
4 x 2	
4 x 3	
Total Quadrilaterals	

Counting Quadrilaterals

Connecting Learning

1. How many different-sized squares are in the grid? What are they?

2. How many squares of each size are there? What patterns do you see in these numbers?

3. How many squares are there total?

4. How many different-sized rectangles are in the grid? What are they?

5. How many rectangles of each size are there? What patterns do you see in these numbers?

6. What is the total number of quadrilaterals in the grid?

7. How many squares do you think would be in a 5 x 5 grid? ...rectangles? ...total quadrilaterals? Why?

Dueling Dice

Topic
Probability

Key Question
Which die should you pick to roll the highest number most of the time?

Learning Goals
Students will:
1. play a game using four non-standard dice,
2. evaluate the results of the game, and
3. use what they learned to develop a strategy that allows them to win most of the time.

Guiding Document
NCTM Standards 2000*

- *Collect data using observations, surveys, and experiments*
- *Represent data using tables and graphs such as line plots, bar graphs, and line graphs*
- *Propose and justify conclusions and predictions that are based on data and design studies to further investigate the conclusions or predictions*
- *Describe events as likely or unlikely and discuss the degree of likelihood using such words as certain, equally likely, and impossible*
- *Build new mathematical knowledge through problem solving*

Math
Probability
Logical thinking
Data analysis

Integrated Processes
Observing
Comparing and contrasting
Collecting and recording data
Interpreting
Analyzing
Generalizing
Applying

Problem-Solving Strategies
Organize the information
Use logical thinking
Use manipulatives

Materials
Wooden cubes (see *Management 1*)
Student pages

Background Information
This activity originated with a Stanford University statistician, Bradley Efron, who designed the game as a study in probability. Using four nonstandard dice that they construct themselves, students will play a game that involves both careful logical consideration and a little bit of luck.

The object of the game is to roll the highest number. One student begins by choosing one of the four non-standard dice. The second student then chooses a die and both roll. The highest roll wins. Six rolls are made using the same set of dice; each roll is recorded in one of the tables on the third student page. For the next game, the students switch who chooses first and repeat the process.

What becomes apparent after playing several games is that the person choosing first is at a distinct disadvantage. No matter which die they choose, the person choosing second can select a die with a two-thirds probability of winning. Once students realize this, only a series of less probable rolls will make the person who chooses second lose.

To see the reasons for this, every possible combination of two dice must be considered. When the probabilities for a given die winning in each combination are examined, it becomes clear that one die is always at a distinct advantage. For an exploration of the theoretical probabilities, see the *Extension*. (This exploration is only intended for advanced students who are able to understand the topics it presents.)

Management
1. If possible, use wooden cubes or other uniform cube shapes to make the non-standard dice. Students can write the numbers on the faces as instructed on the first student page. Another option is to cover the faces of standard dice with self-adhesive dots on which the revised numbers are written. Each pair of students will need four cubes.
2. If wooden cubes are not available, copy the page of dice patterns onto card stock for each group. Students can cut apart and assemble the cubes with tape or glue sticks.
3. This activity is designed to be played in pairs. Each set of two students will need one copy of the first two student pages and one set of non-standard dice.

Procedure
1. Have students get into pairs and distribute the first student page and the materials for constructing the non-standard dice to each group.

2. Once groups have constructed their sets of four dice, hand out the remaining student pages—one copy for each student.

3. Go over the rules and be sure students understand the procedure. Allow time for them to play six games and record their rolls and who won in each case.

4. After playing six games, students should begin to develop some strategies for winning the most often. The table and questions on the last two student pages should help students recognize and verbalize these strategies.

5. Before answering the questions on the final student page, have students play at least four more games to test their strategies. (In these subsequent games, students do not need to roll six times with the same set of dice, but they should be sure to switch who chooses first each game.)

6. Close with a time of discussion in which students share their strategies and what they learned about probability.

Connecting Learning

1. In the six games you played in *Part Two*, who won more often, the person choosing first or the person choosing second? Why?

2. In the games you played in *Part Three*, who won more often, the person choosing first or the person choosing second? Why?

3. Do you think it matters if you choose first or second? [Yes.] Why or why not? [If you choose second, you can always select a die that will give you a greater chance of winning when paired with the die chosen by the first person.]

4. Describe your chances of winning the game if you choose your die first. [Unlikely if the person choosing second selects properly.] ...if you choose second. [Likely if the correct die is selected.]

5. Is it impossible for the person who chooses first to win? Why or why not?

6. If the person going first chose Die A, which die would you choose? Why?

7. What if he or she chose Die B? ...Die C? ...Die D? Justify your responses.

8. Were you able to develop a strategy for choosing your die? Please describe it.

Extension

For advanced students, distribute the extension pages and have them explore the theoretical probabilities involved with each die.

* Reprinted with permission from *Principles and Standards for School Mathematics*, 2000 by the National Council of Teachers of Mathematics. All rights reserved.

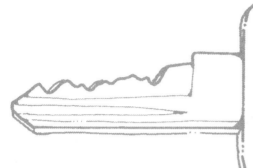 

Dueling Dice

> ## Key Question
> Which die should you pick to roll the highest number most of the time?

Learning Goals

Students will:

1. play a game using four non-standard dice,
2. evaluate the results of the game, and
3. use what they learned to develop a strategy that allows them to win most of the time.

Dueling Dice

This activity has several parts. Be sure to do each part completely before moving on to the next one.

Part One:
With your partner, make a set of four dice. Label the sides of the dice with the following numbers:

Die A:
0: two sides
4: four sides

Die B:
3: all six sides

Die C:
2: four sides
6: two sides

Die D:
1: three sides
5: three sides

Part Two:
This is a game of chance where you must try to make the odds go in your favor. To begin, Player A chooses one of the four dice. Then Player B chooses one of the remaining three dice. Each player rolls his or her die, and the person with the highest number wins. Roll both dice six times. Use the table for Game One to record which die wins each time. Do this five more times, taking turns choosing first.

Part Three:
Complete the worksheet to determine the number of times that each die won when it was paired with another. When you have completed this page, play the game a few more times. Try to use what you have learned to develop a strategy for winning most of the time.

Part Four:
Answer the questions about the game and how the information you collected affected your strategy.

Dueling Dice Part One

Cut out the four shapes on this page, being careful not to cut off the tabs.

Fold each shape into a cube, gluing the tabs to the inside in the order that they are numbered. When finished, you should have the four dice (A, B, C, and D) necessary for this game.

Dueling Dice Part Two

Record the letter of the die chosen by each player for each game. Note: The player who chooses first changes each game. In the *Winner* column record the letter of the die that had the highest number for each of the six rolls. At the bottom of each table, record the number of times each player won in that game. At the bottom of the page record the number of games each player won overall.

Player A's die: _____
Player B's die: _____

Game One

Roll	Winner
1	
2	
3	
4	
5	
6	

Player A won _____ times
Player B won _____ times

Player B's die: _____
Player A's die: _____

Game Two

Roll	Winner
1	
2	
3	
4	
5	
6	

Player A won _____ times
Player B won _____ times

Player A's die: _____
Player Bs die: _____

Game Three

Roll	Winner
1	
2	
3	
4	
5	
6	

Player A won _____ times
Player B won _____ times

Player B's die: _____
Player A's die: _____

Game Four

Roll	Winner
1	
2	
3	
4	
5	
6	

Player A won _____ times
Player B won _____ times

Player A's die: _____
Player B's die: _____

Game Five

Roll	Winner
1	
2	
3	
4	
5	
6	

Player A won _____ times
Player B won _____ times

Player B's die: _____
Player A's die: _____

Game Six

Roll	Winner
1	
2	
3	
4	
5	
6	

Player A won _____ times
Player B won _____ times

Player A won ____ games overall.   Player B won ____ games overall.

There were ____ games that were ties.

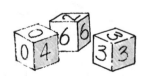

Dueling Dice Part Three

Using the information from the tables on the previous page, fill in the table below to compare the number of times each die won in the different games you played. Starting with *Game One*, record the number of times each die won out of the total number of rolls in the game. This number should be represented as a fraction such as 2/6 or 5/6.

Game	Die	Wins/Total
One		/6
One		/6
Two		/6
Two		/6
Three		/6
Three		/6
Four		/6
Four		/6
Five		/6
Five		/6
Six		/6
Six		/6

Look at the results of your first six games in the table. Use what you see and what you noticed while you were playing to develop a strategy that will help you win most of the time. Try to use this strategy as you play the game a few more times with your partner.

Dueling Dice Part Four

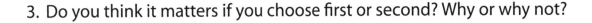

1. In the six games you played in *Part Two*, who won more often, the person choosing first or the person choosing second? Why?

2. In the games you played in *Part Three*, who won more often, the person choosing first or the person choosing second? Why?

3. Do you think it matters if you choose first or second? Why or why not?

4. If the person going first chose Die A, which die would you choose? Why?

5. What if he or she chose Die B? …Die C? …Die D? Justify your responses.

6. Were you able to develop a strategy for choosing your die? Please describe it.

Dueling Dice Extension

In the diagrams of the four dice here, the six faces have been numbered. This allows you to look at all of the possible rolls that can occur.

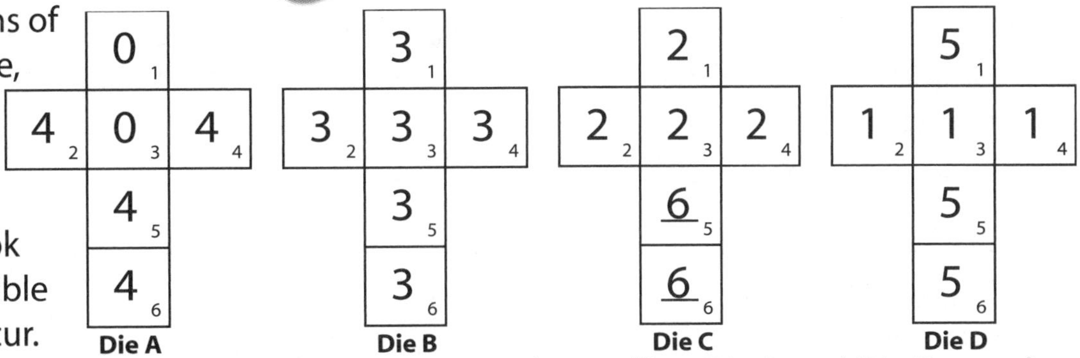

Die A
0_1 / 4_2 0_3 4_4 / 4_5 / 4_6

Die B
3_1 / 3_2 3_3 3_4 / 3_5 / 3_6

Die C
2_1 / 2_2 2_3 2_4 / 6_5 / 6_6

Die D
5_1 / 1_2 1_3 1_4 / 5_5 / 5_6

All of the possible combinations that can occur when rolling Die A and Die B together are listed here. Although the same sets of numbers occur repeatedly (0, 3, and 3, 4), each possible roll listed is unique. For example, a pairing of 4_2 and 3_4 is different than a pairing of 4_2 and 3_1.

Combination	Die A	Die B
1	0_1	3_1
2	0_1	3_2
3	0_1	3_3
4	0_1	3_4
5	0_1	3_5
6	0_1	3_6
7	0_3	3_1
8	0_3	3_2
9	0_3	3_3
10	0_3	3_4
11	0_3	3_5
12	0_3	3_6
13	4_2	3_1
14	4_2	3_2
15	4_2	3_3
16	4_2	3_4
17	4_2	3_5
18	4_2	3_6

Combination	Die A	Die B
19	4_4	3_1
20	4_4	3_2
21	4_4	3_3
22	4_4	3_4
23	4_4	3_5
24	4_4	3_6
25	4_5	3_1
26	4_5	3_2
27	4_5	3_3
28	4_5	3_4
29	4_5	3_5
30	4_5	3_6
31	4_6	3_1
32	4_6	3_2
33	4_6	3_3
34	4_6	3_4
35	4_6	3_5
36	4_6	3_6

Die A wins 24 times out of 36.

Die B wins 12 times out of 36.

Dueling Dice Extension

Using the tables on the previous page as a model, choose a different pairing of dice and complete the tables below. Be sure to indicate which two dice you are using in the appropriate spaces.

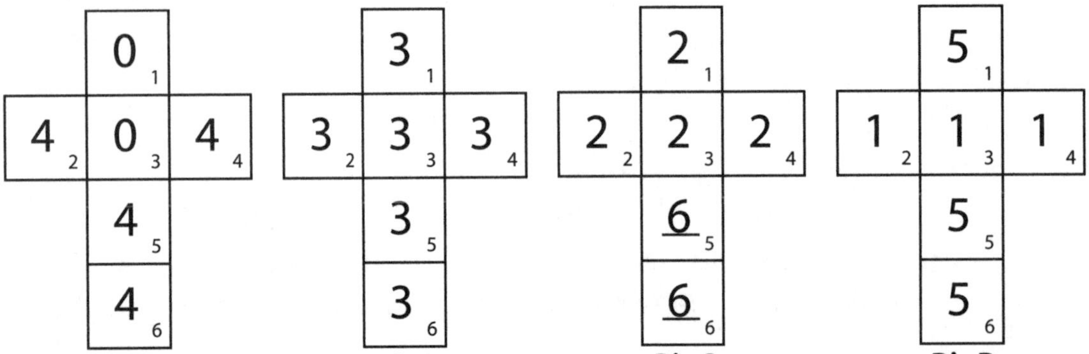

	0 (1)		
4 (2)	0 (3)	4 (4)	
	4 (5)		
	4 (6)		

Die A

	3 (1)		
3 (2)	3 (3)	3 (4)	
	3 (5)		
	3 (6)		

Die B

	2 (1)		
2 (2)	2 (3)	2 (4)	
	6 (5)		
	6 (6)		

Die C

	5 (1)		
1 (2)	1 (3)	1 (4)	
	5 (5)		
	5 (6)		

Die D

Combination	Die ___	Die ___
1		
2		
3		
4		
5		
6		
7		
8		
9		
10		
11		
12		
13		
14		
15		
16		
17		
18		

Combination	Die ___	Die ___
19		
20		
21		
22		
23		
24		
25		
26		
27		
28		
29		
30		
31		
32		
33		
34		
35		
36		

Die ___ wins ___ times out of 36.

Die ___ wins ___ times out of 36.

Dueling Dice Extension

The tables at the bottom of the page will help you determine the probability that each die will win when it is paired with every other die. As you have discovered, there are 36 different ways a pair of dice can be rolled. However, since these dice have only one or two numbers on their six sides, many of the possible two-number combinations are the same. In the tables, you will record each different two-number combination that a given pair of dice would yield, the number of times each combination would occur (out of 36), and which die would win in each situation.

In the *# combinations* columns, record each different two-number combination possible with those two dice. In the *Frequency* column, record the number of times that two-number combination can occur. In the *Winner* column, record which die has the higher number in that combination. The first table has been done for you as an example.

Die A: 0₁ | 4₂ 0₃ 4₄ | 4₅ | 4₆

Die B: 3₁ | 3₂ 3₃ 3₄ | 3₅ | 3₆

Die C: 2₁ | 2₂ 2₃ 2₄ | 6₅ | 6₆

Die D: 5₁ | 1₂ 1₃ 1₄ | 5₅ | 5₆

# combinations: Die A	Die B	Frequency	Winner
0	3	12	B
4	3	24	A

# combinations: Die A	Die C	Frequency	Winner

# combinations: Die A	Die D	Frequency	Winner

# combinations: Die B	Die D	Frequency	Winner

# combinations: Die B	Die C	Frequency	Winner

# combinations: Die C	Die D	Frequency	Winner

Dueling Dice Extension

Using the values from the tables on the previous page, fill in the table of theoretical probabilities below. Probabilities are often written as fractions. For example, to say that the probability of rolling a one on Die D is three out of six we would write $P(1) = 3/6$. For each combination, write the total number of times each die would win over the total number of possible combinations. As you already discovered, there are always 36 possible combinations when two dice are rolled. The number from the *Frequency* column on the previous page indicates the number of times out of 36 that a given die will win. The first combination has been done for you as an example.

Combination	Probability of winning	
A, B	$P(A) = 24/36$	$P(B) = 12/36$
A, C	$P(A) =$	$P(C) =$
A, D	$P(A) =$	$P(D) =$
B, C	$P(B) =$	$P(C) =$
B, D	$P(B) =$	$P(D) =$
C, D	$P(C) =$	$P(D) =$

Dueling Dice Extension

1. Based on the data you have collected, what is the most important factor that will determine who wins most of the time? Why?

2. How does knowing the probabilities that a given die will win change the way you play this game?

3. Outline the strategy you would use if you always had to pick first. Defend your reasoning.

4. How do the theoretical probabilities compare to the actual results you got when playing this game?

5. What are some factors that could account for these differences?

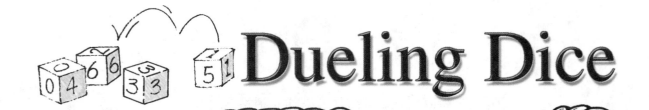

Dueling Dice

Connecting Learning

1. In the six games you played in *Part Two*, who won more often, the person choosing first or the person choosing second? Why?

2. In the games you played in *Part Three*, who won more often, the person choosing first or the person choosing second? Why?

3. Do you think it matters if you choose first or second? Why or why not?

4. Describe your chances of winning the game if you choose your die first. ...if you choose second.

5. Is it impossible for the person who chooses first to win? Why or why not?

6. If the person going first chose Die A, which die would you choose? Why?

7. What if he or she chose Die B? ...Die C? ...Die D? Justify your responses.

8. Were you able to develop a strategy for choosing your die? Please describe it.

Problem-Solving Strategies
Guess and Check

Sometimes to solve a problem, it's a good idea to just make a guess. Then you can check your answer to see if it's correct. If it's not, make another guess using what you learned from your first guess. Soon you will find the correct answer. This is a good strategy to use when you don't know how to approach a problem. It's also good when the problem is very complicated or has lots of answers.

Making Change

Topic
Problem solving

Key Question
If you are paying with a 10-dollar bill, what prices will have the same digits in the cost and in the amount of change you receive?

Learning Goal
Students will determine all of the possible combinations in which the cost of an item and the change received have the same digits when paying with a 10-dollar bill.

Guiding Documents
Project 2061 Benchmark
- *Mathematics is the study of many kinds of patterns, including numbers and shapes and operations on them. Sometimes patterns are studied because they help to explain how the world works or how to solve practical problems, sometimes because they are interesting in themselves.*

NCTM Standards 2000*
- *Build new mathematical knowledge through problem solving*
- *Solve problems that arise in mathematics and in other contexts*
- *Apply and adapt a variety of appropriate strategies to solve problems*

Math
Number and operations
    subtraction
Number sense
    decimals
Problem solving

Integrated Processes
Observing
Collecting and recording data
Comparing and contrasting
Analyzing

Problem-Solving Strategies
Guess and check
Look for patterns
Organize the information

Materials
Student pages

Background Information
Imagine for a minute that you are in a store in Oregon (a state with no sales tax). You wish to purchase an item that costs five dollars, and the only money you have is a 10-dollar bill. How much money will you receive in change? Of course, the answer is five dollars. There is nothing very exciting about that problem from a computational standpoint; $10 - 5 = 5$ is a basic subtraction fact. But what if the problem is seen from a different point of view? A cost of $5.00 yields change of $5.00. All of the digits in the cost and the change are the same. Are there any other costs that will yield change with the same digits? If the digits must be in the same order, then the answer is no, but if the order of the digits is unimportant, several different solutions are possible. This is the problem that students are asked to explore in this activity.

Management
1. Students should be allowed to work on this activity in small groups so that they can share their ideas and help each other look for patterns in the solutions.
2. Each student will need his or her own copy of the student pages.
3. The first student page presents the problem to students and challenges them to find solutions, without giving much structure. The second student page asks a series of questions and is intended for students to use once they have discovered their solutions to help them explore the patterns that are present.
4. While some students may be uncomfortable with the open-ended approach of this activity, it is good for them to be challenged with problems that do not follow a prescribed procedure. At first, students will likely approach this problem by trial and error—plugging in numbers and seeing if any work. They should be encouraged that this is a perfectly valid problem-solving method. Once they have discovered one or two solutions using this method, however, encourage them to think about the problem logically and try to develop a systematic approach for finding the rest of the solutions.

Procedure

1. Divide students into groups and distribute the first student page. Explain the problem and give groups time to work toward finding all possible solutions.
2. After groups have made several discoveries, distribute the second student page to each student.
3. Once students have had time to discover their solutions and answer the questions on the second student page, close with a time of class discussion during which students can share any additional patterns they discovered as well as the methods they used to arrive at their solutions.

Connecting Learning

1. What patterns do you see when you look at the number of cents?
2. What patterns do you see when you look at the number of dollars?
3. What patterns do you see when you look at the sum of the numbers in each amount?
4. Based on these patterns, do you think you have found all of the possible solutions? Why or why not?
5. Describe any other patterns or interesting things you discovered while working on this problem.

Extension

Discover the solutions for paying with a $100 bill. These solutions can then be compared and contrasted with the solutions for $10.

Solutions

There are 11 instances in which the digits in the cost and the digits in the change are the same. These solutions follow a very predictable pattern and have several interesting characteristics.

Paying with $10.00

Cost	Change
$9.05	$0.95
$8.15	$1.85
$7.25	$2.75
$6.35	$3.65
$5.45	$4.55
$5.00	$5.00
$4.55	$5.45
$3.65	$6.35
$2.75	$7.25
$1.85	$8.15
$0.95	$9.05

Following is a brief discussion of some of the patterns that students should discover in these values. *(Note: the $5.00 cost is an exception to these patterns.)*

- The sum of the digits in each solution is always equal to 14. (9 + 0 + 5 = 14, 8 + 1 + 5 = 14, etc.)
- The number of cents is always divisible by 5.
- The first two numbers in each value are all of the two number combinations that sum 9. (0 + 9, 1 + 8, 2 + 7, etc.)
- Reversing the first two digits of the cost gives you the change.

* Reprinted with permission from *Principles and Standards for School Mathematics*, 2000 by the National Council of Teachers of Mathematics. All rights reserved.

Making Change

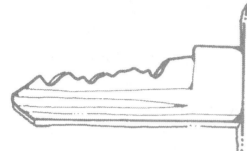

Key Question

If you are paying with a 10-dollar bill, what prices will have the same digits in the cost and in the amount change you receive?

Learning Goal

Students will:

determine all of the possible combinations in which the cost of an item and the change received have the same digits when paying with a 10-dollar bill.

SALE
$10.00
OR LESS

NO TAX

Making Change

If you pay for a five-dollar item with a 10-dollar bill, you will receive five dollars in change. Both the cost of the item ($5.00) and the change ($5.00) have the same digits—two zeros and one five. The same is true for an item that costs $4.55, for which you receive $5.45 in change. Again, the cost and the change have the same digits—one four and two fives. What other prices are there where the cost of the item and the change received have the exact same digits? (Keep in mind, the digits do not have to be in the same order.) Record each solution you discover in the space below. Organize your answers in a logical fashion and look for patterns in your solutions.

Extra challenge: What if you were paying for an item with a $100 bill? How many instances can you find where the price of the item and the change have the same digits? How do these values compare to the values for $10.00?

Making Change

Use these questions to help you search for patterns in your solutions.

1. What patterns do you see when you look at the number of cents?

2. What patterns do you see when you look at the number of dollars?

3. What patterns do you see when you look at the sum of the numbers in each amount?

4. Based on these patterns, do you think you have found all of the possible solutions? Why or why not?

5. Describe any other patterns or interesting things you discovered while working on this problem.

Making Change

Connecting Learning

1. What patterns do you see when you look at the number of cents?

2. What patterns do you see when you look at the number of dollars?

3. What patterns do you see when you look at the sum of the numbers in each amount?

4. Based on these patterns, do you think you have found all of the possible solutions? Why or why not?

5. Describe any other patterns or interesting things you discovered while working on this problem.

Sam's SWEET SHOP

Topic
Problem solving

Key Question
How can you change the prices in Sam's shop so that everything is more (or less) expensive, but no new numbers are used?

Learning Goal
Students will manipulate the cost of three items to make each more and less expensive than the original price without using any new numbers.

Guiding Document
NCTM Standards 2000*
- *Build new mathematical knowledge through problem solving*
- *Solve problems that arise in mathematics and in other contexts*
- *Apply and adapt a variety of appropriate strategies to solve problems*

Math
Number and operations
　　addition
　　subtraction
Number sense
　　decimals
Problem solving

Integrated Processes
Observing
Comparing and contrasting
Organizing
Relating

Problem-Solving Strategies
Guess and check
Use manipulatives
Organize the information

Materials
Number cards
Student pages

Background Information
　　The setting for the problem is a candy shop, in which a thrifty (or perhaps just lazy) shopkeeper wants to change his prices, but doesn't want to buy

any new numbers. This reduces him to rearranging the numbers he already has. His current prices are as follows: $1.10—one giant jawbreaker, $1.28—one bag of gummy bears, $1.36—one chocolate pecan turtle. Students are challenged to come up with as many different solutions as they can for two different scenarios: making all three prices higher, and making all three prices lower. Additional stipulations say that only the cents (not the dollars) can be manipulated, and the relative prices of the items must remain the same.

Management
1. To facilitate students finding solutions with the greatest ease, have them cut small cards out of scratch paper and label them with the six numbers used: 0, 1, 2, 3, 6, 8. Having number cards to manipulate will allow students to quickly try many possible number combinations and only write down valid solutions.
2. This activity is presented in two parts. Be sure that students have ample time to work on the solution-discovery portion before moving on to the analysis portion. There are more than 25 different solutions for making the prices more expensive, and at least nine solutions for making the prices less expensive. Groups will benefit from having time to think about ways to systematically check their solutions and determine if they have found all possibilities.

Procedure
1. Have students get into groups and distribute the first student page. Allow students to make number cards to assist them as they search for solutions.
2. Allow plenty of time for groups to discover and record solutions.
3. Distribute the final two student pages. Have groups work together to answer the questions.
4. Conduct a time of class sharing and allow groups to share their discoveries and insights with the rest of the class.
5. Make a class list of solutions by compiling information from each group. (This provides an excellent opportunity for discussing ways to systematically organize data.)

Connecting Learning

1. How many solutions did you find that made all three prices more expensive? Do you think you have found them all? Why or why not?

2. How many solutions did you find that made all three prices less expensive? Do you think you have found them all? Why or why not?

3. What number(s) could be in the tenths place for the jawbreaker price when it had to be less expensive? Why? [Zero is the only possibility. The only way to have a value less than $1.10 is to put the zero in the tenths place.]

4. Could you have the number two in the tenths place for the gummy bears price when you were trying to make it more expensive? Why or why not? [No. There is no nine available to change the $1.28 to $1.29, so the only way to make the gummy bears more expensive is to change the tenths place number to a three or a six. (Be sure that students recognize that these are the only two possibilities. The tenths place digit cannot be an eight because that would make it impossible for the chocolate turtle to be more expensive than the gummy bears.)]

5. What number(s) had to go in the tenths place for the chocolate turtle price when you were trying to make it more expensive? Why? [Either six or eight. The only way to make the price more expensive with a three in the tenths place is to have an eight in the hundredths place. If this is the case, there is no way to also make the other two prices more expensive and maintain the relative costs.]

6. If a customer buys one of each item, what is the most money that Sam could make after increasing his prices? How many different price combinations will give him this much? [The most that can be made is $4.73. This total can be reached by any combination that uses three, six, and eight as the tenths place digits. There are six possible combinations that do this.]

7. How does this amount compare to how much he would have made with the original prices? [The total made on the original prices is $3.74. That means the increase in profit is $0.99. ($4.73 – $3.74 = $0.99)]

8. If you were Sam's customer and wanted to get one of each item for the least amount of money, how would you set the prices? How much would these prices save you when compared to the original prices? What other ways could you set the prices and save this same amount of money? [The least amount of money that it is possible to spend on all three items is $3.47. This is a savings of $0.27 ($3.74 – $3.47 = $0.27). This total can be reached by any combination that uses zero, one, and two as the tenths place digits. There are six possible combinations that do this.]

9. Write down the cost for purchasing all three items at the original price, the most expensive possible price, and the least expensive possible price. What do you notice about the digits in all of the prices? How can you explain this? [Original price: $3.74; most expensive price: $4.73; least expensive price: $3.47. The same three digits appear in all three prices. Having the same three digits in all three values does not happen with most number combinations. It just so happens that the numbers chosen for this activity have that unique characteristic.]

Extensions

1. Create a different problem by having students gather sets of numbers from the real world such as gas prices or clothing prices.

2. Remove one of the restrictions and allow students to change the dollar amount instead of just the cents.

3. Challenge students to come up with combinations of numbers that would have only a single solution for each scenario.

Solutions

This list of solutions is partial.

Original Prices:
$1.10—One giant jawbreaker
$1.28—One bag of gummy bears
$1.36—One chocolate pecan turtle

Each price higher:

Jawbreaker:	$1.12	$1.12	$1.12	$1.20
Gummy bears:	$1.38	$1.30	$1.30	$1.31
Turtle:	$1.60	$1.68	$1.86	$1.68

Jawbreaker:	$1.21	$1.30	$1.31	$1.32
Gummy bears:	$1.63	$1.61	$1.62	$1.61
Turtle:	$1.80	$1.83	$1.80	$1.80

Each price lower:

Jawbreaker:	$1.03	$1.03	$1.06	$1.06
Gummy bears:	$1.16	$1.18	$1.18	$1.13
Turtle:	$1.28	$1.26	$1.23	$1.28

Jawbreaker:	$1.08	$1.08	$1.08	$1.08
Gummy bears:	$1.26	$1.16	$1.13	$1.16
Turtle:	$1.31	$1.23	$1.26	$1.32

Key Question

How can you change the prices in Sam's shop so that everything is more (or less) expensive, but no new numbers are used?

Learning Goal

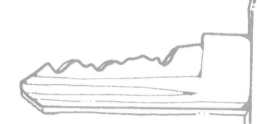

manipulate the cost of three items to make each more and less expensive than the original price without using any new numbers.

Part One

Sam is a thrifty shopkeeper. He wants to change the prices on his candy menu, but he doesn't want to buy any new numbers. Can you help him rearrange his prices so that everything is more expensive? You can only change the cents; each item must still be more than one dollar but less than two dollars. Each item must also keep the same relative cost—the turtle must always cost more than the gummy bears, which must always cost more than the jawbreaker.

Part Two

Once you have discovered as many solutions as you can, rearrange the original prices so that everything is less expensive. Again, the relative costs must stay the same.

One Giant Jawbreaker A DELICIOUSLY ROUND CONCOCTION OF FLAVOR	$1.10
One Bag of Gummy Bears OVER 30 OF THE GUMMIEST BEARS TO BE FOUND ANYWHERE	$1.28
One Chocolate Pecan Turtle PECAN, CARAMEL AND THE FINEST IMPORTED SWISS CHOCOLATE	$1.36

Find as many solutions as you can for both problems and record them in the space provided.

Answer these questions once you have recorded all of the solutions you can find. Discuss your responses within your group, and be prepared to share your thoughts with the rest of the class.

1. How many solutions did you find that made all three prices more expensive? Do you think you have found them all? Why or why not?

MMM... JAWBREAKER.

2. How many solutions did you find that made all three prices less expensive? Do you think you have found them all? Why or why not?

3. What number(s) could be in the tenths place for the jawbreaker price when it had to be less expensive? Why?

4. Could you have the number two in the tenths place for the gummy bears price when you were trying to make it more expensive? Why or why not?

5. What number(s) had to go in the tenths place for the chocolate turtle price when you were trying to make it more expensive? Why?

6. If a customer buys one of each item, what is the most money that Sam could make after increasing his prices? How many different price combinations will give him this much? Show your work.

7. How does this amount compare to how much he would have made with the original prices? Show your work.

8. If you were Sam's customer and wanted to get one of each item for the least amount of money, how would you set the prices? How much would these prices save you when compared to the original prices? What other ways could you set the prices and save this same amount of money?

9. Write down the cost for purchasing all three items at the original price, the most expensive possible price, and the least expensive possible price. What do you notice about the digits in all of the prices? How can you explain this?

Connecting Learning

1. How many solutions did you find that made all three prices more expensive? Do you think you have found them all? Why or why not?

2. How many solutions did you find that made all three prices less expensive? Do you think you have found them all? Why or why not?

3. What number(s) could be in the tenths place for the jawbreaker price when it had to be less expensive? Why?

4. Could you have the number two in the tenths place for the gummy bears price when you were trying to make it more expensive? Why or why not?

5. What number(s) had to go in the tenths place for the chocolate turtle price when you were trying to make it more expensive? Why?

Connecting Learning

6. If a customer buys one of each item, what is the most money that Sam could make after increasing his prices? How many different price combinations will give him this much?

7. How does this amount compare to how much he would have made with the original prices?

8. If you were Sam's customer and wanted to get one of each item for the least amount of money, how would you set the prices? How much would these prices save you when compared to the original prices? What other ways could you set the prices and save this same amount of money?

9. Write down the cost for purchasing all three items at the original price, the most expensive possible price, and the least expensive possible price. What do you notice about the digits in all of the prices? How can you explain this?

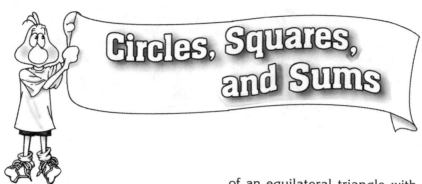

Circles, Squares, and Sums

Topic
Mathematical microworld

Key Question
How can you arrange the specified numbers in the arrays so that any number placed in a square is the sum of the numbers in circles connected to that square?

Learning Goal
Students will search for solutions to a mathematical microworld and make observations about what they discover.

Guiding Document
NCTM Standards 2000*
- *Build new mathematical knowledge through problem solving*
- *Solve problems that arise in mathematics and in other contexts*
- *Apply and adapt a variety of appropriate strategies to solve problems*

Math
Number and operations
    addition
Problem solving

Integrated Processes
Observing
Comparing and contrasting
Recording
Organizing
Analyzing

Problem-Solving Strategies
Guess and check
Use manipulatives

Materials
Number cards (see *Management 2*)
Student pages

Background Information.
    A mathematical microworld is an environment governed by specific rules and structures. For example, the microworld might consist of nine spaces in the shape of an equilateral triangle with a goal of arranging the numbers from one to nine in the spaces so that the sum of the numbers on each side is the same. The original idea for this microworld came from an activity in the *Games* magazine, but the end result has turned out to be quite different. In *Circles, Squares, and Sums*, the microworlds have some spaces that are squares, and some that are circles. The goal is to arrange the numbers in the microworlds so that any number placed in a square is the sum of the numbers in the circles connected to that square.

Management
1. There are three challenges presented in this activity, two that use the numbers one to six and one that uses the numbers one to nine. The two challenges that use the numbers one to six are presented as warm-ups, and each have only one unique solution (a solution that is different from others even when flipped and/or rotated). These easier warm-ups should help your students prepare for the main challenge, which uses more numbers and has multiple solutions.
2. The easiest way for students to work on this activity is to have them cut pieces of scratch paper that will fit into the spaces in the microworlds and number them from one to nine. Having number cards allows students to easily move the numbers around on their papers and saves both ends of the pencil.
3. You may want to allow students to work on the main challenge for short periods of time over several days. This will help to ease any frustration and will hopefully allow for more solutions to be discovered.

Procedure
1. Distribute the first student page and have students make number cards that will fit in the spaces of the microworlds.
2. Go over the instructions and be sure students understand the challenge. Have them work on the warm-ups and record their solutions.
3. Distribute the main challenge and solutions pages. Allow students time to work on the problem and discover solutions.

4. Have students share their solutions. Compile a class list that reflects all solutions discovered. Discuss any patterns or "rules" that students noticed while working on the problem.

Connecting Learning

1. How many solutions were there for each of the warm-up challenges? Why?
2. How many solutions were you able to find for the main challenge? Do you think you have found them all? Why or why not?
3. What number(s) always appear in the bottom left circle? Do you think it is possible to have other numbers there? Why or why not?
4. What is the lowest number that you can have in a square? Why?
5. What is the highest number that you can have in a circle? Why?
6. What is the lowest number that you can have in either of the two center left squares? Why?
7. What are some other interesting discoveries that you made about your solutions?
8. What other questions would you like to explore using this microworld?

Solutions

This list of solutions is complete to the best of our knowledge. Your students may discover solutions that are not listed here.

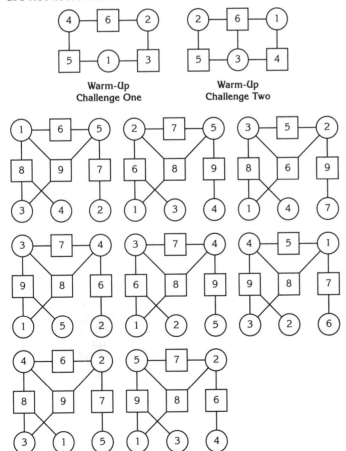

This diagram indicates the numbers that can go in each space in a given solution of the main challenge.

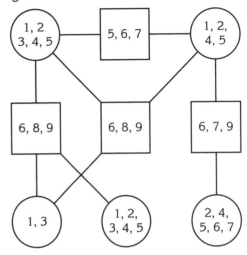

Following are a few observations that can be made about the arrangement of the numbers in this array:

- The way the array is designed, there are two squares that each have three circles connected to them (the center square, and the left center square). The smallest number that can go in one of these squares is six, because six is the smallest number that can be made by summing three smaller numbers $(1 + 2 + 3 = 6)$.
- The number seven can never go in either of the squares that have three circles connected to them.
- The smallest number that can go in a square is five. However, the only square in which five can go is the top center square.
- The largest number that can go in a circle is seven. However, the only circle in which seven can go is the bottom right circle.
- The number one cannot go in the bottom right circle because it must be a part of the sum for at least one of the three-number sum squares.
- The number one or the number three must always be in the bottom left circle.

*   Reprinted with permission from *Principles and Standards for School Mathematics*, 2000 by the National Council of Teachers of Mathematics. All rights reserved.

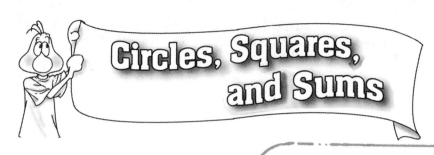

Circles, Squares, and Sums

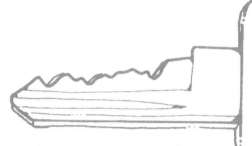
Learning Goal

Students will:

search for solutions to a mathematical microworld and make observations about what they discover.

Circles, Squares, and Sums

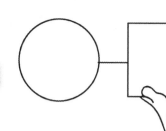

Warm-Up
Arrange the numbers from one to six in the microworlds below so that any number in a square is the sum of the numbers in the circles connected to that square. For example, if you were to place the number 5 in the top center square, you would have to place either the 2 and the 3 or the 1 and the 4 in the circles to the right and left. Record your solutions.

Challenge One:

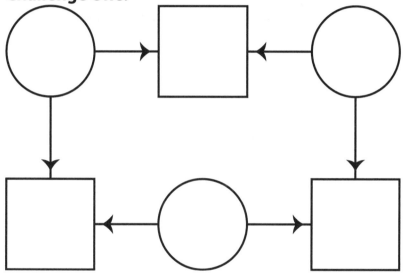

Solution

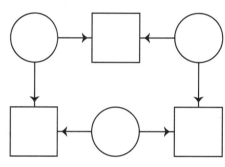

Challenge Two:

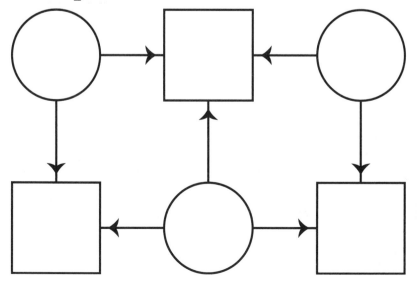

Solution

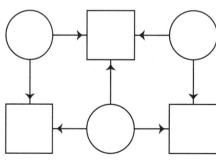

Circles, Squares, and Sums

Main Challenge

Now that you have completed the warm-ups, you should be ready to move on to something more challenging. Arrange the numbers from one to nine in the microworld below so that any number in a square is the sum of the numbers in the circles connected to that square. Unlike the warm-up challenges, there are multiple solutions to this problem. Record each solution that you discover in the spaces on the following page.

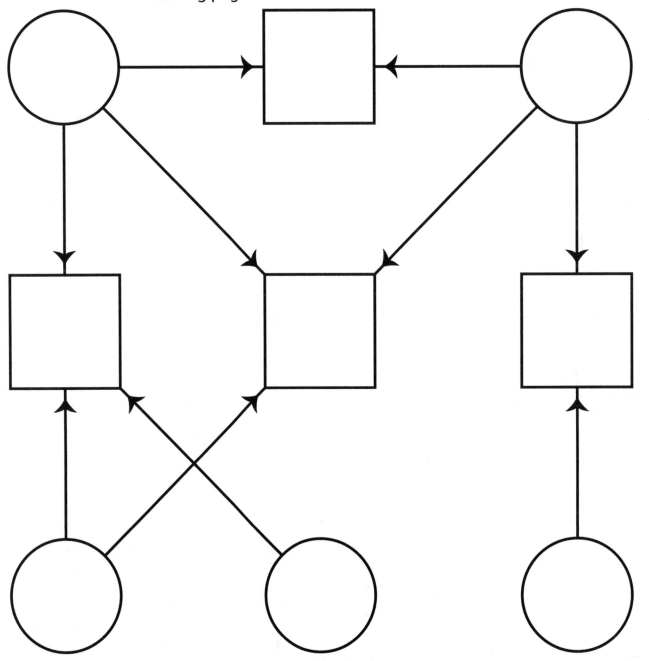

Circles, Squares, and Sums   Solutions

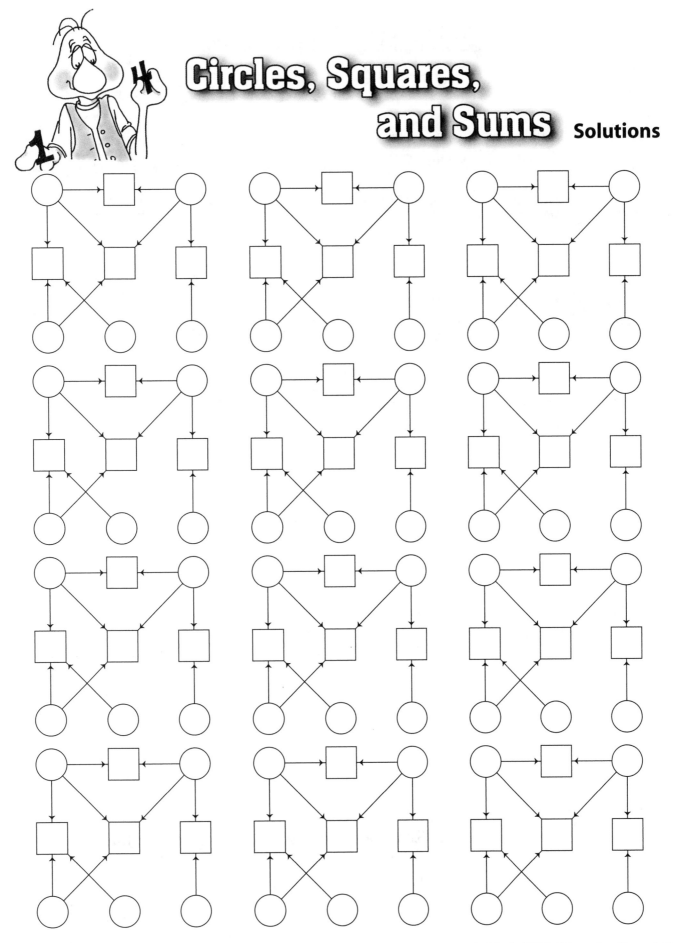

Circles, Squares, and Sums

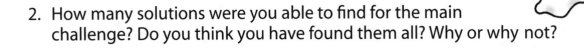

Answer the following questions after you have found at least three solutions to the main challenge.

1. How many solutions were there for each of the warm-up challenges? Why?

2. How many solutions were you able to find for the main challenge? Do you think you have found them all? Why or why not?

3. What number(s) always appear in the bottom left circle? Do you think it is possible to have other numbers there? Why or why not?

4. What is the lowest number that you can have in a square? Why?

5. What is the highest number that you can have in a circle? Why?

6. What is the lowest number that you can have in either of the two center left squares? Why?

7. Write some other interesting discoveries that you made about your solutions.

174

Circles, Squares, and Sums

Connecting Learning

1. How many solutions were there for each of the warm-up challenges? Why?

2. How many solutions were you able to find for the main challenge? Do you think you have found them all? Why or why not?

3. What number(s) always appear in the bottom left circle? Do you think it is possible to have other numbers there? Why or why not?

4. What is the lowest number that you can have in a square? Why?

5. What is the highest number that you can have in a circle? Why?

6. What is the lowest number that you can have in either of the two center left squares? Why?

7. What are some other interesting discoveries that you made about your solutions?

8. What other questions would you like to explore using this microworld?

THREE-DIGIT DIVISIBILITY DILEMMA

Topic
Problem solving

Key Question
How many answers can you find to the riddle?

Learning Goals
Students will:
1. find as many answers as they can to an open-ended mathematical riddle,
2. organize their solutions, and
3. look for patterns to determine if they have found them all.

Guiding Document
NCTM Standards 2000*
* *Build new mathematical knowledge through problem solving*
* *Solve problems that arise in mathematics and in other contexts*
* *Apply and adapt a variety of appropriate strategies to solve problems*
* *Monitor and reflect on the process of mathematical problem solving*

Math
Number and operations
    divisibility
Pattern recognition
Problem solving

Integrated Processes
Observing
Comparing and contrasting
Recording
Organizing
Analyzing
Generalizing

Problem-Solving Strategies
Guess and check
Look for patterns
Organize the information

Materials
Student pages

Background Information
In this activity, students are asked to find as many numbers as they can that meet the following three criteria: has three-digits, each digit is unique, is divisible by 11. However, students need to know the meaning of *divisible* before starting the activity. The concept of divisibility is a key one that plays an important role in algebra. When 143 is divided by 11 the answer is 13

with no remainder. Mathematicians say that 143 is *divisible* by 11. What they mean when they say this is that it divides it evenly with no remainder. While you can certainly divide 143 by 10 (the answer is 14 with a remainder of 3), a mathematician would say that 143 is *not* divisible by 10—this means that it cannot be divided without a remainder. Numbers that divide evenly into larger numbers are called *divisors*. Divisors and divisibility are closely related to *factors* and *multiples*. In the example, 143 is a multiple of 11 and 13 and these two numbers are factors of 143. A divisor of a larger number is also a factor of that number. These concepts play a key role in algebra and this activity should help your students construct a deeper understanding of them.

Procedure
1. Distribute the student page and discuss the problem, making sure everyone understands the criteria for a correct solution.
2. Invite students to make predictions as to how many solutions might be possible. Record these predictions on the board for later reference.
3. Allow time for students to work on the problem and find solutions. Once a few solutions have been discovered, encourage students to look for patterns and strategies that might help them find more solutions.
4. When students are confident they have discovered all possible solutions, have them share and compile a master list. Encourage students to share the strategies and patterns they used to help them solve the problem.

Connecting Learning
1. How did you approach this problem? How did your method compare to the methods used by others?
2. How many solutions did you discover? Do you think you have found them all? Why or why not?
3. What method(s) did you use to organize your solutions?
4. Did you find any patterns in your solutions?

Solutions
There are 64 solutions that meet all three criteria posed in the riddle.

132	209	308	407	506	605	704	803	902
143	231	319	418	517	627	715	814	913
154	253	341	429	528	638	726	825	924
165	264	352	451	539	649	748	836	935
176	275	374	462	561	671	759	847	946
187	286	385	473	572	682	781	869	957
198	297	396	495	583	693	792	891	968
				594				

Some patterns in the solutions

If the numbers are arranged in a chart by all the possible 3 digit numbers divisible by 11 and the repeating digits are not left out, some patterns can be observed.

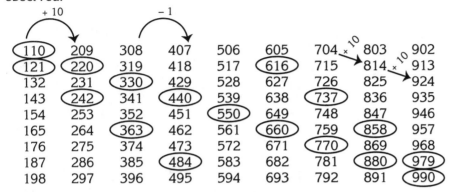

- As you move across the chart horizontally, the digit in the hundreds place increases by one and the digit in the ones place decreases by one.
- As you move along any diagonal from top left to bottom right, the numbers increase by 10.
- Each column has two numbers with repeating digits except the 500s, which only has one number with the same digit used more than once.
  In the 100s column, the first two numbers contain repeating digits.
  In the 200s, the second and fourth numbers contain repeating digits.
  In the 300s, the third and sixth numbers contain repeating digits.
  In the 400s, the fourth and eighth numbers contain repeating digits.
  In the 500s, only the fifth number has a repeating digit.
  In the 600s, the second and sixth numbers contain repeating digits.
  In the 700s, the fourth and seventh numbers contain repeating digits.
  In the 800s, the sixth and eighth numbers contain repeating digits.
  In the 900s, the eighth and ninth numbers contain repeating digits.

THREE-DIGIT DIVISIBILITY DILEMMA

Learning Goals

Students will:

1. find as many answers as they can to an open-ended mathematical riddle,
2. organize their solutions, and
3. look for patterns to determine if they have found them all.

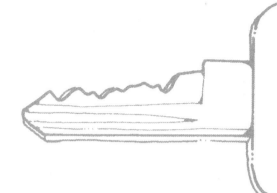

WHO AM I?

THREE-DIGIT DIVISIBILITY DILEMMA

Who am I?
- I have three-digits.
- Each of my digits is different.
- I am divisible by 11.

The above riddle has many different solutions. (For example, 352 and 781 are both correct.) This poses a dilemma. How many answers are there to this riddle?

Your challenge is to see how many solutions you can find. With some mathematical thinking and organizational skills, you may be able to find all the solutions. Use the space below and the back of this sheet to show your work.

THREE-DIGIT DIVISIBILITY DILEMMA

Connecting Learning

1. How did you approach this problem? How did your method compare to the methods used by others?

2. How many solutions did you discover? Do you think you have found them all? Why or why not?

3. What method(s) did you use to organize your solutions?

4. Did you find any patterns in your solutions?

Problem-Solving Strategies
Use Logical Thinking

Sometimes a problem requires logical thinking. You must find an answer when you are missing some of the information. You must make inferences based on what you know. Often logic problems have many clues. Sometimes grids are used to organize the clues. Other times manipulatives are used.

SQUARE GRID LOGIC

Topic
Logical thinking

Key Question
How can you arrange numbers in the grids so that the same number does not appear in the same row or column and all of the clues are true?

Learning Goals
Students will:
1. fill a 3 x 3 square grid with three each of the numbers one, two, and three so that the same number does not appear in the same row or column;
2. arrange the numbers so that the series of clues given are true; and
3. repeat this challenge with a 4 x 4 square.

Guiding Document
NCTM Standards 2000*
- *Solve problems that arise in mathematics and in other contexts*
- *Apply and adapt a variety of appropriate strategies to solve problems*
- *Select and use various types of reasoning and methods of proof*

Math
Logical thinking
Number and operations
 addition
Problem solving

Integrated Processes
Observing
Comparing and contrasting
Organizing
Recording

Problem-Solving Strategies
Use logical thinking
Use manipulatives

Materials
Number cards
Scissors
Student pages

Background Information
This activity was inspired by a game from the March 2003 *Games* magazine called "That's Really Sum-Thing!" The problem combines logic, problem solving, and basic computation in an engaging setting. This version has been significantly simplified from the original to make it appropriate for elementary students.

The initial challenge is to fill a 3 x 3 square grid with three each of the numbers one, two, and three so that the same number does not appear in the same row or column (the same number may appear in the same diagonal).

1	3	2
2	1	3
3	2	1

3	1	2
1	2	3
2	3	1

2	1	3
3	2	1
1	3	2

There are many ways in which it is possible to do this, as you can see in the examples above; however, there is an additional twist to the problem. A series of clues is given that describes the arrangement of the numbers by identifying two or more squares that add up to a specific sum. There is only one solution that meets the conditions of all of these clues, as well as the conditions that no number may appear twice in the same row or column.

Management
1. A sheet of number cards is provided for students to use as they search for solutions to this problem. These cards should be copied onto card stock to make them easier to handle. Make enough copies so that each student can have one set of numbers.
2. This activity can be done individually or with students working together in small groups.

Procedure
1. Distribute the first student page and one set of number cards to each student. Have the students cut apart the cards and go over the instructions.
2. Allow time for students to solve the problem and record their solutions.
3. Distribute the second student page and allow time for them to solve the 4 x 4 grid.

4. If desired, give students the final page and have them create their own problems to trade with classmates.
5. Discuss the solutions and the methods students used to arrive at those solutions.

Connecting Learning

1. How did you solve the problems?
2. What kinds of information did you get from the clues? How did this information help you? [For example, in the first problem, the first clue tells you that the sum of the squares A2 and A3 is five. Since one, two, and three are the only numbers that can fill the grid, A2 and A3 must contain the numbers two and three $(2 + 3 = 5)$. Because the same number cannot appear twice in the same column, A1 must contain the number one.]
3. Would you have been able to solve the problems without using the number cards? Why or why not?

Solutions

The solutions for both the 3 x 3 and 4 x 4 grid are shown below.

2	3	1
3	1	2
1	2	3

2	3	1	4
4	1	3	2
3	2	4	1
1	4	2	3

*   Reprinted with permission from *Principles and Standards for School Mathematics*, 2000 by the National Council of Teachers of Mathematics. All rights reserved.

Key Question

How can you arrange numbers in the grids so that the same number does not appear in the same row or column and all of the clues are true?

Learning Goals

Students will:

1. fill a 3 x 3 square grid with three each of the numbers one, two, and three so that the same number does not appear in the same row or column;
2. arrange the numbers so that the series of clues given are true; and
3. repeat this challenge with a 4 x 4 square.

Copy this page on card stock. Each student needs one set of number cards.

1	1	1	1	1	1	1	1
2	2	2	2	2	2	2	2
3	3	3	3	3	3	3	3
4	4	4	4	4	4	4	4
1	1	1	1	1	1	1	1
2	2	2	2	2	2	2	2
3	3	3	3	3	3	3	3
4	4	4	4	4	4	4	4

SQUARE GRID LOGIC

The grid below must be filled with three each of the numbers 1, 2, and 3 so that the same number does not appear in any one row or column. (The same number may be in the same diagonal.) The arrangement of the numbers must also match the clues given.

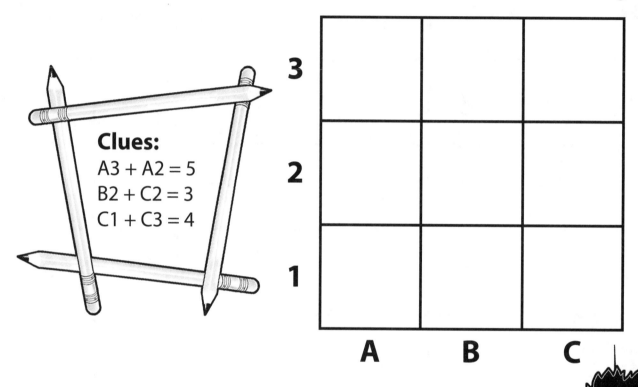

Clues:
A3 + A2 = 5
B2 + C2 = 3
C1 + C3 = 4

Describe the process you went through to solve this problem.

SQUARE GRID LOGIC

The grid below must be filled with four each of the numbers 1, 2, 3, and 4 so that the same number does not appear in any one row or column. (The same number may be in the same diagonal.) The arrangement of the numbers must also match the clues given.

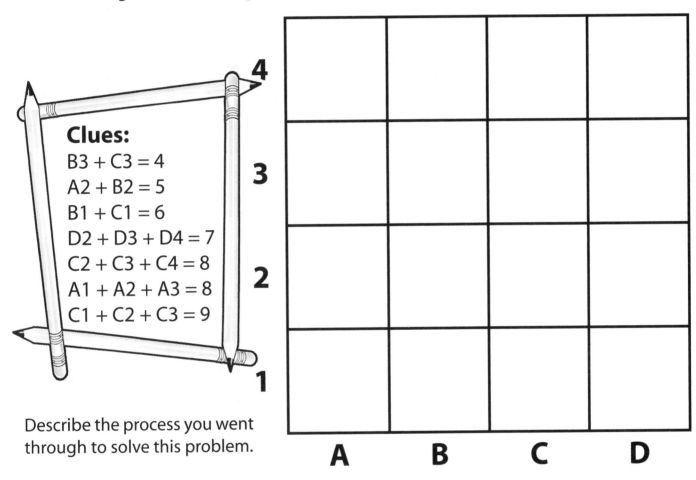

Clues:

B3 + C3 = 4
A2 + B2 = 5
B1 + C1 = 6
D2 + D3 + D4 = 7
C2 + C3 + C4 = 8
A1 + A2 + A3 = 8
C1 + C2 + C3 = 9

Describe the process you went through to solve this problem.

How was solving this problem the same as solving the first problem? How was it different?

Which problem was more difficult? Why?

SQUARE GRID LOGIC

Arrange the numbers in the grid so that no number appears more than once in the same row or column. Record this arrangement of numbers on a piece of scratch paper. Write a series of clues like the ones in the sample problems that would allow someone else to find your arrangement of numbers. Give your puzzle to a classmate and see if he or she can find the solution you came up with. If not, try rewriting or adding clues until your puzzle can be solved.

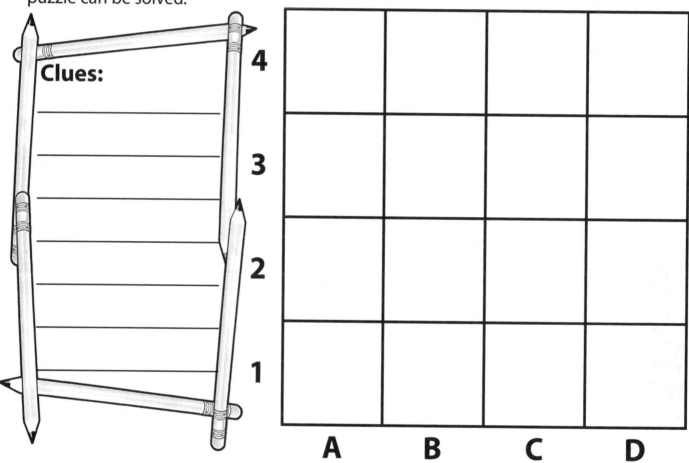

Clues:

4

3

2

1

A   B   C   D

Describe the process you went through to come up with your clues.

Connecting Learning

1. How did you solve the problems?

2. What kinds of information did you get from the clues? How did this information help you?

3. Would you have been able to solve the problems without using the number cards? Why or why not?

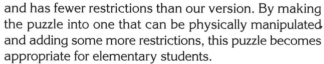

THE MISSING PIECE

Topic
Logical thinking

Key Question
How can you put the puzzle pieces together and determine which is the "missing piece?"

Learning Goals
Students will:
1. use puzzle pieces to construct four shapes while following certain rules,
2. determine the piece from each set that does not belong, and
3. use these "missing pieces" to make an additional shape.

Guiding Document
NCTM Standards 2000*
- *Solve problems that arise in mathematics and in other contexts*
- *Apply and adapt a variety of appropriate strategies to solve problems*
- *Monitor and reflect on the process of mathematical problem solving*
- *Select and use various types of reasoning and methods of proof*

Math
Logical thinking
Problem solving

Integrated Processes
Observing
Comparing and contrasting

Problem-Solving Strategies
Use logical thinking
Guess and check
Use manipulatives

Materials
Puzzle pieces
Scissors
Transparent tape
Student pages

Background Information
The idea for this activity comes from the puzzle "Some of its Parts" in the August 2001 *Games* magazine. The original activity is meant to be done mentally

and has fewer restrictions than our version. By making the puzzle into one that can be physically manipulated and adding some more restrictions, this puzzle becomes appropriate for elementary students.

In this activity, there are four sets of pieces, each of which can be assembled to form one of four larger shapes—a rectangle, a square, a cross, or stairs. There is one catch—one of the pieces in each set is a decoy; it will not fit into the larger shape. The object of the puzzle is to construct the four larger shapes in order to determine which are the *missing pieces*, that is, the pieces that do not belong. The extra feature of our version, which further distinguishes it from its *Games* counterpart, is that once the four missing pieces are discovered, they can be assembled to form one of the larger shapes.

The rules, which must be followed in order to put the shapes together, are simple. Each individual puzzle piece is divided into squares, and each square contains a figure (square, star, octagon, etc.). When putting the puzzle pieces together to form the larger shapes, the pieces may overlap if the figures contained in the overlapping squares are the same. (In each case, at least one piece must overlap another for the solution to be obtained.) The only additional rule is that no figure may appear within a larger shape more than once. Students will discover that there may be several ways in which the pieces fit together to make the larger shape, but only one of these ways uses each figure only once.

Once students have found the solution for each of the larger shapes, they can be challenged to use the four missing pieces to construct another shape. This additional shape is one of the four that is made by the other puzzle pieces.

Management
1. Copy the page of puzzle pieces onto card stock. Each student will need his or her own copy of this page.
2. Students should work on these challenges individually.

Procedure
1. Distribute the page of puzzle pieces and scissors to each student. Have them cut out the shapes and then distribute the student pages.
2. Go over the rules as a class and be sure that everyone understands how the pieces can be put together.

3. Allow time for students to find solutions. Once they discover a solution, have them tape the pieces in place on the student page to make a record of the solution.
4. Challenge students to complete the extra challenge in which they use the missing pieces to create an additional shape.
5. Have students share their solutions and discuss the processes they went through as they searched for the solutions.

Connecting Learning
1. What methods did you use to solve these problems?
2. How successful were your methods at helping you find the correct solutions?
3. How many squares must overlap using the missing pieces? How do you know?
4. Based on this, how many squares will there be in the final shape?
5. Which of the four large shapes has that number of squares?

Solutions
Shown are the pieces and solution for each shape, as well as the extra shape that can be formed by all of the *missing* pieces. In each case, the individual pieces have been given shading to indicate their positions. Overlapping squares and the *missing* pieces have no shading.

Stairs

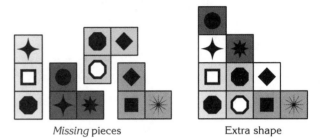

Original pieces   Solution   *Missing* piece

The four *missing* pieces can be assembled to form a second staircase as shown here.

Missing pieces   Extra shape

* Reprinted with permission from *Principles and Standards for School Mathematics*, 2000 by the National Council of Teachers of Mathematics. All rights reserved.

Rectangle

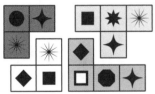

Original pieces   Solution   *Missing* piece

Square

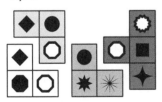

Original pieces   Solution   *Missing* piece

Cross

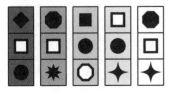
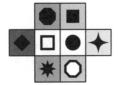

Original pieces   Solution   *Missing* piece

THE MISSING PIECE
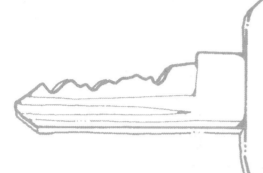

Learning Goals

Students will:

1. use puzzle pieces to construct four shapes while following certain rules,
2. determine the piece from each set that does not belong, and
3. use these "missing pieces" to make an additional shape.

THE MISSING PIECE

There are four sets of pieces shown below, each of which can be used to make the shape listed above it. The pieces are all marked with a variety of figures. Cut out each set, being sure to keep the sets separate. Follow the directions on the next student page.

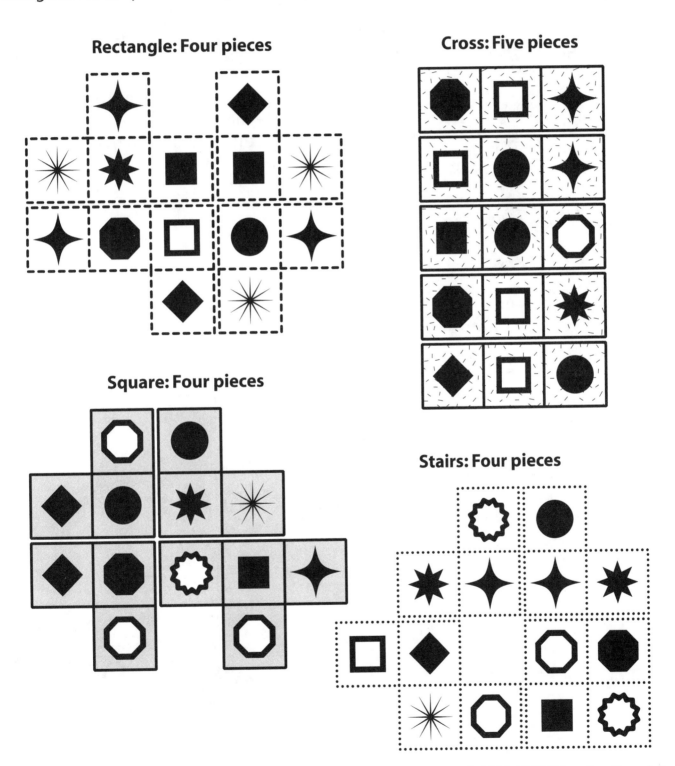

Rectangle: Four pieces

Cross: Five pieces

Square: Four pieces

Stairs: Four pieces

THE MISSING PIECE

One of the pieces that you cut out to make each shape doesn't belong. Determine which should be the "missing piece" by following these rules:

- Completely fill in each grid (shown at the left) using all but one of the pieces you cut out (shown at the right).
- No figure (star, square, octagon, etc.) may appear in a completed grid more than once.
- Pieces may overlap if the figures in the overlapping squares are the same.
- There will always be exactly one piece left over (the "missing piece").

Once you have determined a solution, set aside the "missing piece" from that shape, and glue or tape the pieces into the grid as they belong.

1. Rectangle

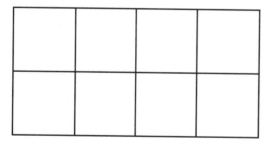

2. Square

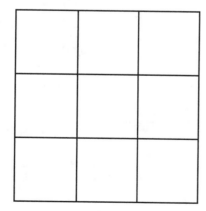

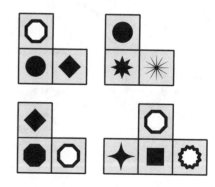

SOLVE IT! 5th

194

© 2006 AIMS Education Foundation

THE MISSING PIECE

3. Cross

4. Stairs

Extra Challenge: The four "missing pieces" can be assembled to make one of the four shapes (rectangle, square, cross or stairs) by following the same rules. Which shape is it, and how can it be done? Once you find the solution, glue or tape the pieces together on the back of this paper.

THE MISSING PIECE

Connecting Learning

1. What methods did you use to solve these problems?

2. How successful were your methods at helping you find the correct solutions?

3. How many squares must overlap using the missing pieces? How do you know?

4. Based on this, how many squares will there be in the final shape?

5. Which of the four large shapes has that number of squares?

Zoo's Clues

Topic
Logical thinking

Key Question
How can you use descriptions of the zoo to figure out where everything is located?

Learning Goal
Students will use various descriptions of the zoo to determine the locations on an unmarked map of the zoo.

Guiding Document
NCTM Standards 2000*
- *Solve problems that arise in mathematics and in other contexts*
- *Apply and adapt a variety of appropriate strategies to solve problems*
- *Select and use various types of reasoning and methods of proof*

Math
Logical thinking
Problem solving

Integrated Processes
Observing
Comparing and contrasting
Organizing
Recording
Inferring
Applying

Problem-Solving Strategies
Use logical thinking
Organize the information

Materials
Student pages

Background Information
This activity is a logic problem that will challenge students' critical thinking and analysis skills. *Zoo's Clues* gives students an unmarked map of a zoo that has the various enclosures and locations lettered. There are three descriptions of the zoo that offer clues as to where the different animals are located. Students must use the information in the descriptions to correctly label the map.

Management
1. There are two different versions of the problem given. The easier version is labeled *Zoo's Clues Challenge One* and the more advanced version is labeled *Zoo's Clues Challenge Two*. Use the appropriate version(s) for your students.
2. This problem can be approached either as an open-ended experience, or as a more structured one depending on individual needs. Students should work together in pairs or small groups of no more than three or four.
3. In order to successfully facilitate this activity, you should solve the problems yourself before giving them to your students. This will allow you to direct their thinking in the right direction and to point out some of the clues they may have missed that will give them the information they need.

Procedure
1. Distribute the appropriate student pages and have students get into small groups.
2. Go over the instructions and be sure everyone understands the task.
3. Provide time for the students to read the clues and develop a method for organizing the information to find the solutions.
4. Have groups share their solutions and their methods for arriving at those solutions. If there are any differences among the groups' answers, determine the correct solution as a class.

Connecting Learning
1. How were you able to identify the different locations on the map?
2. Which locations did you find hardest to determine? Why?
3. Which were easiest to determine? Why?
4. What method did your group use to keep track of the clues?
5. How does this method compare to the one used by other groups?
6. Do you think one method is more effective than another? Why or why not?

Extension
Have students assign different locations to the animals and make new clue statements for the maps.

Solutions

Zoo's Clues Challenge One
A: Tropical rainforest
B: Monkeys, apes, orangutans
C: Giraffes
D: Reptile house
E: Penguins
F: Walruses
G: Polar Bears

Zoo's Clues Challenge Two
A: Aviary
B: Refreshments stand
C: Deer
D: Monkeys, apes, orangutans
E: Seals
F: Reptile house
G: Giraffes
H: Big cats (lions, leopards, cheetahs)
I: Kangaroos
J: Elephants

* Reprinted with permission from *Principles and Standards for School Mathematics*, 2000 by the National Council of Teachers of Mathematics. All rights reserved.

Zoo's Clues

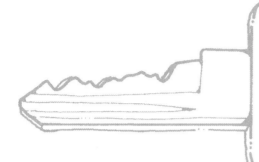

Key Question
How can you use descriptions of the zoo to figure out where everything is located?

Learning Goal

Students will:

use various descriptions of the zoo to determine the locations on an unmarked map of the zoo.

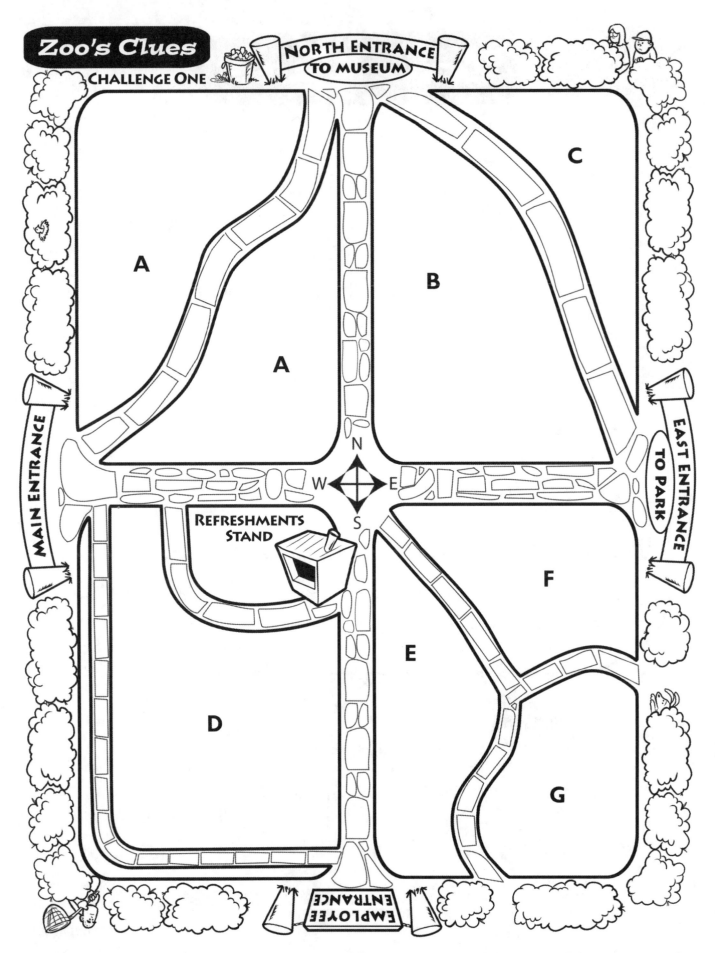

Zoo's Clues

You have received an unmarked map of the zoo. It shows where the various pens, enclosures, walkways, entrances, and exits are located. Your challenge is to identify each of the following animal locations on the map:

- Walruses
- Monkeys, apes, orangutans
- Penguins
- Tropical rainforest
- Giraffes
- Reptile house
- Polar bears

Use these three descriptions of the zoo to help you with your task.

Marisa, a zoo employee

Napoleon, the largest of the emperor penguins, was playing with his baby in the water this morning when I came in. I'm glad that the penguin tank is right by my entrance. I often get to see them doing the things they only do when there are no visitors staring at them.

I had to clean the giraffe cage right when I got to work this morning. I hate doing that first because it is all the way on the other side of the zoo from where I come in. To make things worse, the monkeys had been throwing their food across the path again. The floor of the giraffes' area was covered with orange peels and half-eaten bananas. Hopefully, next time I have to clean the giraffe pen the monkeys will be better behaved.

201

Suzanne, a mother

The zoo was so crowded today! The line coming from the refreshments stand was blocking the entrance to the reptile house, and reached almost to the main entrance. Samantha ran off while we were looking at the penguins and I lost her in the crowd. I found her 10 minutes later at the end of the walkway between the polar bears and the walruses. She was sitting by the fence that separates the park from the zoo, crying. After I found her, we walked by the monkeys on our way to the museum, where we spent the rest of the day.

Jerome, a student

We went to the zoo for our class field trip today. My favorite part was the tropical rainforest. We saw all kinds of birds and animals that live in the tropics all together. There is a long windy path that you go down. You look at stuff on both sides. When we got out of the rainforest we went across a walkway to the monkeys. I didn't like them. The orangutan threw a piece of banana at me. The Polar corner was nice though. They have all of the cold-weather animals together in the same section—the walruses, the penguins, and the polar bears. We didn't get to see the polar bears for very long because they are in the back corner, and we had to go back to the bus.

Zoo's Clues

You can solve logic problems in many ways. One way is by a process of elimination. You can record what you know about each animal in a table. If enough clues tell you where an animal is NOT, eventually, you will know where it IS. Another way is by making a grid. You can use the grid to mark off where things are and where they are not. Use the space below to show your work. You can make a table, a grid, or do something different.

203

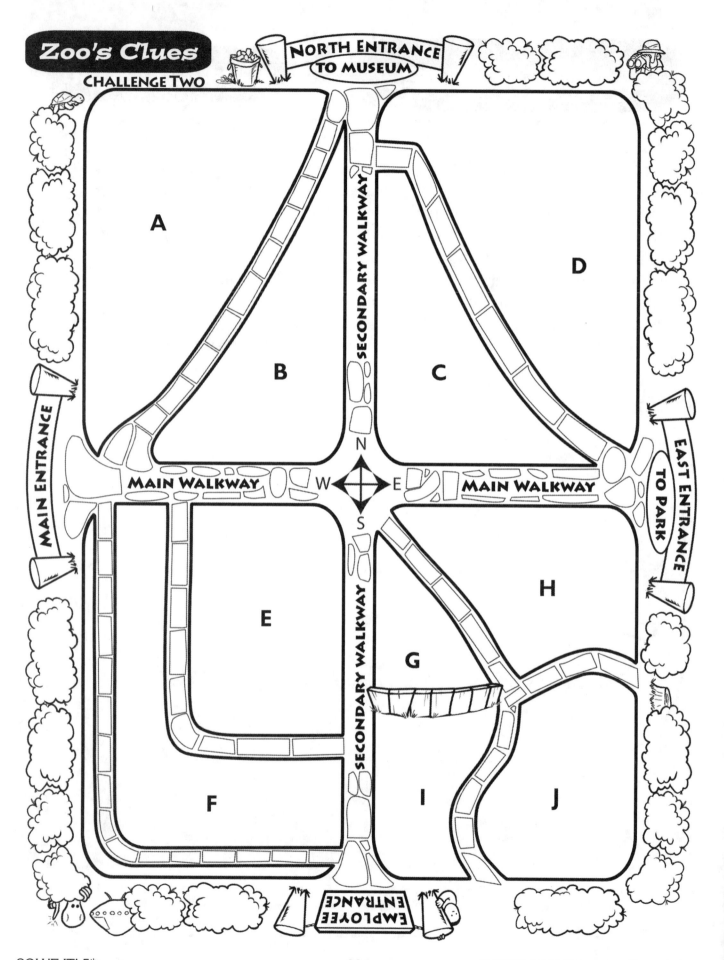

Zoo's Clues

Challenge Two

You have received an unmarked map of the zoo. It shows where the various pens, enclosures, walkways, entrances, and exits are located. Your challenge is to identify each of the following animals and locations on the map:

- Refreshments stand
- Kangaroos
- Elephants
- Big cats (lions, leopards, and cheetahs)
- Deer and buffalo

- Monkeys, apes, orangutans
- Reptile house
- Aviary
- Giraffes
- Seals

Use these three descriptions of the zoo to help you with your task.

Xavier, a zoo employee

Joey, the largest of the gray kangaroos didn't look so good when I came to work today. He's always the first animal I see when I come in to the zoo. Usually he's active and happy to see me, but today he wouldn't even come to the fence when I called him. I hope visitors haven't been feeding him candy again. That's what happened last time he got sick. The other possibility is that the giraffes have been dropping some of their acacia leaves into his pen again. We may need to raise the fence between their two pens. I'll have to check on Joey later today after I make my rounds.

Today I have to clean the aviary. I hate doing it because it's always so crowded, since it's just inside the main entrance. There is always a ton of trash lying around. It seems like people come straight from the refreshments stand and i to the aviary, since the two are just across the path from each other on the same side of the main walkway. I wish people would learn to use the trashcans!

Serena, a student

Our class took a field trip to the zoo today. In the morning we went to see the aviary and the reptile house. Those were both just inside the entrance, right across the main walkway from each other. From the reptile house we went to see all of the different monkeys. We sure had to walk a long way to get to them! They are in the exact opposite corner of the zoo. The good thing was, after we saw the monkeys we were right by the park. We went there to eat our lunch, since we were all getting pretty hungry. After lunch, we went to the big cats and the elephants. I went exploring down one of the walkways in the front of the elephant enclosure, but it was a dead end that went to the fence between the zoo and the park. On the way back out we saw the seals, and then went directly across the main walkway to get a snack for the trip home. It was a real fun day, even though the orangutan threw an orange peel at me.

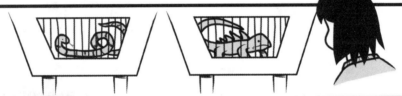

David, a father

After spending the morning in the museum, we used the rest of the afternoon to see the zoo. It has an interesting layout. The whole western half has no land mammals, while the eastern half has only land mammals. We started with all of the monkeys because they were immediately to the east of the entrance we came through. I noticed a few orange peels and half-eaten bananas in the deer pen. They must have been thrown across the small path by the orangutans. I also noticed trash on the side of the deer pen that faces the secondary walkway. It must be from people who bought things at the refreshments stand, which is just to the west.

From there we went to the big cats and then took a brief walk in the park, since the exit was right there. Except for the monkeys, they seem to have kept most of their African game together. With the exception of the kangaroos, everything in that southeast corner is from Africa. We had already seen the reptile house and aviary, so we went back to our car and went home.

Zoo's Clues

You can solve logic problems in many ways. One way is by a process of elimination. You can record what you know about each animal in a table. If enough clues tell you where an animal is NOT, eventually, you will know where it IS. Another way is by making a grid. You can use the grid to mark off where things are and where they are not. Use the space below to show your work. You can make a table, a grid, or do something different.

Zoo's Clues

Connecting Learning

1. How were you able to identify the different locations on the map?

2. Which locations did you find hardest to determine? Why?

3. Which were easiest to determine? Why?

4. What method did your group use to keep track of the clues?

5. How does this method compare to the one used by other groups?

6. Do you think one method is more effective than another? Why or why not?

Problem-Solving Strategies
Wish for an Easier Problem

2+2

Sometimes a problem has lots of data or big numbers. It can seem too hard to do. This is when you can "wish for an easier problem." You can use smaller numbers instead of the big ones. You can think about how to solve the problem instead of the numbers and data. This will help you see how to solve a simpler version of a harder problem.

HOW THICK IS IT?

Topic
Problem solving

Key Question
What are some ways you can think of to find the thickness of a single sheet of paper?

Learning Goals
Students will:
1. brainstorm a variety of methods to determine the thickness of a sheet of paper, and
2. use one of their methods to find the thickness of a sheet of paper.

Guiding Document
NCTM Standards 2000*
• *Build new mathematical knowledge through problem solving*
• *Solve problems that arise in mathematics and in other contexts*
• *Apply and adapt a variety of appropriate strategies to solve problems*
• *Monitor and reflect on the process of mathematical problem solving*

Math
Measurement
Estimation
Problem solving

Integrated Processes
Observing
Comparing and contrasting
Collecting and recording data
Interpreting

Problem-Solving Strategy
Wish for an easier problem

Materials
Measurement materials (see *Management 2*)
Student page

Background Information
In this activity, students are asked to think of, and then list, various ways to determine the thickness of a piece of paper. After doing this, they are to pick one of these methods, apply it, and come up with an answer.

One method is to write a letter to a paper company asking for this information. Another way is to use a micrometer—a tool for measuring tiny distances. These devices are not generally available in elementary schools, but could be borrowed from high school shop departments. Another method is to use a notebook with a known number of pages and measure its thickness with the covers folded back. From this measurement the thickness per page can be calculated. A similar method is to get a ream of paper and measure its height and then divide by the number of sheets. Yet another method is to place an object of known height, such as a centicube, on a table and then stack paper until the stack is equal to the height of the object. The thickness of a single sheet can then be calculated. Another possibility is to use a hand lens and a finely-marked ruler—stacking paper until it is equal to the smallest unit on the ruler. Another way to solve this problem would be to measure a certain number of pages in a book and then calculate the thickness of a single page. The advantage of this method is that the pages are numbered for you. (Don't forget to use half the value of the page number if the pages are printed front and back—in this case page 100 would actually be on the 50th sheet of paper.)

Management
1. This activity can be done individually, in small groups, or as a whole-class activity.
2. Depending on the methods students come up with, you will need to provide a variety of materials for them to carry out their plans. These might include rulers, reams of paper, centicubes, etc.

Procedure
1. Distribute the student page and allow time for students to brainstorm, either individually, in groups, or as a class.
2. Share some of the methods suggested, and discuss how feasible and appropriate they are to do in the classroom.
3. Have students or groups decide on one method to implement and provide them with the necessary materials. There should be a variety of methods employed so that a comparison can be made between the results.
4. Encourage students to describe their processes in words and pictures/diagrams.

5. When all students or groups have arrived at a thickness for a single sheet of paper, have them share their results.
6. Compare and contrast the values reached by the different methods.

Connecting Learning
1. What are some ways that you could find the thickness of a single sheet of paper?
2. Which of these methods are possible for you to do in the classroom?
3. How effective was the method you chose to use? Were you able to easily determine a value for the thickness of a single sheet of paper?
4. What value did you come up with? How does that compare to the other values reached by your classmates?
5. Which methods that we used gave similar results?
6. Which methods had results that were the most different? What might account for these differences? [different kinds of paper, accuracy of measurements, etc.]
7. Is there one method that you think is the most effective? Explain your thinking.
8. Based on all of the data collected, what is a good estimate of the thickness of a single sheet of paper?

Extensions
1. Determine the thicknesses of different kinds of paper—construction paper, chart paper, card stock, etc.
2. Follow this activity with *Cut and Stack*.

* Reprinted with permission from *Principles and Standards for School Mathematics*, 2000 by the National Council of Teachers of Mathematics. All rights reserved.

HOW THICK IS IT ?

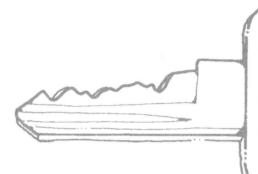

Key Question

What are some ways you can think of to find the thickness of a single sheet of paper?

Learning Goals

Students will:

1. brainstorm a variety of methods to determine the thickness of a sheet of paper, and

2. use one of their methods to find the thickness of a sheet of paper.

HOW THICK IS IT?

How can you find the thickness of a piece of paper?

Think of some ways to do this and list them below.

After you are finished with your list, share your methods with others in class. Discuss the appropriateness of the various methods.

Pick one method and use it to determine the thickness of a piece of paper. Use the back of this page to record your process and findings and then share these with the rest of the class.

213

HOW THICK IS IT?

Connecting Learning

1. What are some ways that you could find the thickness of a single sheet of paper?

2. Which of these methods are possible for you to do in the classroom?

3. How effective was the method you chose to use? Were you able to easily determine a value for the thickness of a single sheet of paper?

4. What value did you come up with? How does that compare to the other values reached by your classmates?

5. Which methods that we used gave similar results?

6. Which methods had results that were the most different? What might account for these differences?

7. Is there one method that you think is the most effective? Explain your thinking.

8. Based on all of the data collected, what is a good estimate of the thickness of a single sheet of paper?

CUT AND STACK

Topic
Problem solving

Key Question
What would be the height of the resulting stack if a sheet of paper were cut in half, the pieces stacked, then cut in half again a total of 25 times?

Learning Goal
Students will determine the height of a stack of paper that would result from cutting a single sheet in half and stacking the resulting pieces 25 times.

Guiding Documents
Project 2061 Benchmark
- *Add, subtract, multiply, and divide whole numbers mentally, on paper, and with a calculator.*

NCTM Standards 2000*
- *Develop fluency in adding, subtracting, multiplying, and dividing whole numbers*
- *Carry out simple unit conversions, such as from centimeters to meters, within a system of measurement*
- *Build new mathematical knowledge through problem solving*
- *Solve problems that arise in mathematics and in other contexts*
- *Apply and adapt a variety of appropriate strategies to solve problems*
- *Monitor and reflect on the process of mathematical problem solving*

Math
Number and operations
   powers of two
Measurement
Problem solving

Integrated Processes
Observing
Collecting and recording data
Analyzing
Applying

Problem-Solving Strategies
Wish for an easier problem
Look for patterns

Materials
Student pages
Calculators, optional
Scissors, optional
Scratch paper, optional

Background Information
This activity provides lots of computational practice in a problem-solving context. When working on the problem posed here, students will do a lot of doubling of numbers. If they try the extra challenge, students will be dividing whole numbers and simple fractions in two.

Cut and Stack is a modification of a classic problem from recreational mathematics. Both the classic problem and this modified version have the same challenge, determining the height of a stack of paper after completing a certain procedure. In this procedure, a large sheet of paper is cut in half. The two resulting pieces are then stacked and a second cut is made dividing each of these pieces in half. The resulting four pieces are stacked and a third cut is made producing eight pieces. This process of cutting and stacking is repeated a pre-determined number of times—50 for the classic problem, but only 25 in this version. This problem is not intended to be done in the real world, since after about six or seven cuts, the stack becomes too thick to cut and the pieces get quite small, making them hard to handle.

Management
1. This activity is closely related to the previous activity—*How Thick Is It?* and the two are meant to be done sequentially. The information gained in the previous activity—the thickness of a single sheet of paper—is used in *Cut and Stack,* so students should do *How Thick Is It?* first. (If you don't have the time to do this, you can give students a predetermined value for paper thickness—approximately 0.1 mm for photocopy paper.)
2. This activity can be done using either an open-ended or a more structured approach. Since the first student page simply introduces the problem, it can be used by itself with students who are already comfortable with the problem-solving process. The second and third pages provide students with the structure needed to help them solve the problem and can be given to those students who require a

215

more structured approach. Choose the approach and pages that best suit your students' needs.

3. Even though the procedure becomes unwieldy after just a small number of cuts and stacks, you may choose to introduce the problem by having your students apply the procedure four or five times to a piece of scratch paper. This will give them a concrete appreciation for the power of doubling and help them understand the problem a bit better.

4. You may wish to give your students calculators to help them with the computation of the large numbers.

Procedure

1. Distribute the appropriate student page(s) to each student. If desired, give students scissors and scratch paper and have them model the problem by cutting and stacking the paper four or five times.

2. Allow time for students to work on the problem and develop their solutions.

3. Have students share both their solutions and the methods they used to arrive at those solutions.

4. Challenge students to work on the second part of the problem in which they determine the size of the paper after the 25 cuts. The fourth student page is provided for this portion of the problem.

5. Close with a final time of class discussion and sharing.

Connecting Learning

1. What method did you use to solve this problem?

2. How many sheets would be in a stack that had been cut five times? [25] ...10 times? [100] ...20 times? [400]

3. What patterns do you see in these numbers? [They are the powers of two.]

4. How did you use the information about the number of sheets in the stack to determine the height of the stack?

5. What would be the height of the stack resulting from 25 cuts? (See *Solutions.*)

6. What answer did you come up with for the extra challenge? (See *Solutions.*)

7. How did you get that answer? How does that compare to the way you got your answer for the main challenge?

8. What other related questions would you like to explore?

Extensions

1. Calculate the height of the stack after 50 cuts.

2. Determine the size of the final pieces of paper after 50 cuts.

3. Determine the size of paper that you would have to start with to end up with pieces that are a specific size (e.g., 1 cm x 1 cm) after five, 10, 15, and 20 cuts.

Solutions

Main Problem

If a large sheet of paper were cut and stacked 25 times, the resulting stack would contain more than 30 million (very small) sheets and be just over two miles tall. Cutting and stacking 50 times would produce over a quadrillion sheets that would be close to 70 million miles tall. The surprising numbers (of sheets) show the power of doubling and they can be represented mathematically by two to the twenty-fifth power (2^{25}) and two to the fiftieth power (2^{50}).

When using 0.1 mm as the thickness for a sheet of paper, a stack height of 3,355,443.2 mm for the 25 cuts can be calculated by multiplying the number of sheets by the thickness of one sheet. This value can be converted into meters by dividing by 1000. Doing this produces a more manageable 3355 meters—when rounded to the nearest meter. The meters can be converted into kilometers by dividing by 1000 once more. This gives an answer of slightly over three and a third kilometers. If you wish to convert kilometers into miles, multiplying 3.355 km by 0.62 (the approximate number of kilometers in a mile) produces an answer of about two miles. The same calculations for 50 cuts produces a *much* more impressive stack that is 112,589,991 kilometers or almost 70 million miles high!

Extra Challenge

If the original sheet were 128 meters long and 64 meters wide, the first cut would produce two sheets 64 meters long and 64 meters wide. The second cut would produce four sheets 64 meters long by 32 meters wide. The third cut would produce eight sheets that are 32 meters long by 32 meters wide. Carrying out this process 25 times shows that the length and width of each of the individual 33,554,432 sheets would be 1/64 meter by 1/64 meter or slightly over a centimeter and a half in length and width. While the cuts produce large numbers of sheets, each of these sheets quickly shrinks in length and width.

CUT AND STACK

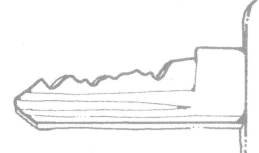

Key Question

What would be the height of the resulting stack if a sheet of paper were cut in half, the pieces stacked, then cut in half again a total of 25 times?

Learning Goal

Students will:

determine the height of a stack of paper that would result from cutting a single sheet in half and stacking the resulting pieces 25 times.

CUT AND STACK

Imagine an enormous sheet of paper as long and wide as a football field, but the same thickness as a normal-sized piece of paper. If this giant sheet of paper were cut in half, the pieces stacked, and then cut in half again, you would have four large sheets of paper. If the resulting stack were cut in half, you would have eight pieces that could be stacked and cut in half again. If this process of cutting and stacking were repeated 25 times, what would be the height of the stack of paper?

Make a guess and then find the answer.
My guess:

Extra challenge: If the original sheet of paper were 128 meters long and 64 meters wide, what would the dimensions of each piece of paper be after the original had been cut in half 25 times?

CUT AND STACK

Imagine an enormous sheet of paper as long and wide as a football field, but the same thickness as a normal-sized piece of paper. If this giant sheet of paper were cut in half, the pieces stacked, and then cut in half again, you would have four large sheets of paper. If the resulting stack were cut in half, you would have eight pieces that could be stacked and cut in half again. If this process of cutting and stacking were repeated 25 times, what would be the height of the stack of paper?

Make a guess and then complete the table and below to find the answer.

My guess: _____

Number of Sheets for 25 Cuts

# of cuts	# of sheets	# of cuts	# of sheets
0	1	13	
1	2	14	
2	4	15	
3	8	16	
4		17	
5		18	
6		19	
7		20	
8		21	
9		22	
10		23	
11		24	
12		25	

CUT AND STACK

Now that you know the number of sheets, you can calculate the height of the stack by multiplying the number of sheets in the stack by the thickness of a single sheet of paper.

_____sheets times _____mm equals a stack height of _____ mm.

You can change the millimeters into meters by dividing the above measurement by 1000 since there are 1000 millimeters in a meter.

_____ mm divided by 1000 equals a stack height of _____meters.

To find the height in kilometers, divide the above answer by 1000 since there are 1000 meters in a kilometer.

_____meters divided by 1000 equals a stack height of _____kilometers.

(You can find out how many miles this is by multiplying the above answer by 0.6 since there are about 0.6 miles in a kilometer.)

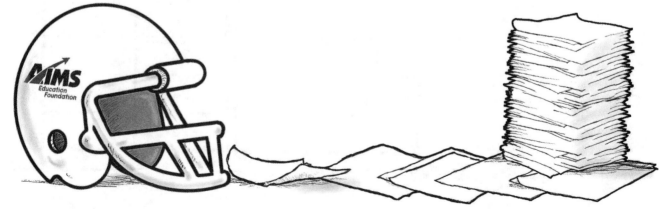

CUT AND STACK

Extra challenge: If the original sheet of paper were 128 meters by 64 meters, what would the length and width of each piece of paper be after the original had been cut in half 25 times?

Paper Dimensions

Number of cuts	Length in meters	Width in meters	Number of cuts	Length in meters	Width in meters
0	128	64	13		
1	64	64	14		
2	64	32	15		
3	32	32	16		
4			17		
5			18		
6			19		
7			20		
8			21		
9			22		
10			23		
11			24		
12			25		

The 25th sheet would be _____ meters long and _____ meters wide.

© 2006 AIMS Education Foundation

CUT AND STACK

Connecting Learning

1. What method did you use to approach this problem?

2. How many sheets would be in a stack that had been cut five times?...10 times? ...20 times?

3. What patterns do you see in these numbers?

4. How did you use the information about the number of sheets in the stack to determine the height of the stack?

5. What would be the height of the stack resulting from 25 cuts?

6. What answer did you come up with for the extra challenge?

7. How did you get that answer? How does that compare to the way you got your answer for the main challenge?

8. What other related questions would you like to explore?

Topic
Problem solving

Key Question
How many pages are in a book numbered consecutively (starting with one) and requiring a total of 3089 digits to paginate?

Learning Goal
Students will determine the number of pages in a book numbered consecutively (starting with one) and requiring a total of 3089 digits to paginate.

Guiding Documents
Project 2061 Benchmark
* *Add, subtract, multiply, and divide whole numbers mentally, on paper, and with a calculator.*

NCTM Standards 2000*
* *Build new mathematical knowledge through problem solving*
* *Solve problems that arise in mathematics and in other contexts*
* *Apply and adapt a variety of appropriate strategies to solve problems*
* *Monitor and reflect on the process of mathematical problem solving*

Math
Problem solving

Integrated Processes
Observing
Recording
Analyzing

Problem-Solving Strategies
Wish for an easier problem
Organize the information

Materials
Student pages
Calculators, optional

Background Information
This activity begins with a multi-step story problem similar to the ones found in many math textbooks, but then extends this problem to create an open-ended one. Students are asked how many pages are in a book numbered consecutively (starting with one) and

requiring a total of 3089 digits to paginate. They are asked to work on the problem and to show how they arrived at their answers, thus emphasizing the process over the product. Students are also encouraged to share how they approached the problem with one another. This discussion helps students develop their mathematical communication skills. This activity gets its open-ended nature by challenging students to come up with extension questions to explore after they have solved the original problem.

Management
1. Students should work on this activity in groups.
2. You may choose to spread this activity over multiple days to allow time for students to explore their extensions in-depth.
3. If desired, make calculators available to students.

Procedure
1. Distribute the student page for *Part One* and go over the challenge as a class.
2. Provide time for groups to work together to discover the solution.
3. Have groups share their solutions, placing emphasis on the problem-solving strategies they used to find their answers.
4. Distribute the student page for *Part Two*. Allow groups to brainstorm a variety of possible extensions for the problem.
5. Have students work on these extensions, perhaps at home or over a period of several days.
6. Close with a final time of discussion and sharing.

Connecting Learning
1. How many pages are there in the book? How do you know?
2. What methods did your group use to arrive at this answer? How do these methods compare to those used by other groups?
3. What extensions did you think of to explore?
4. What did you discover when you explored these extensions?
5. What problem-solving strategies did you use?

Extensions
It is hoped that students will generate questions on their own. However, the following are a few suggestions if they are having trouble thinking of good questions.

223   © 2006 AIMS Education Foundation

1. How many times does the digit nine appear in the pagination? How about the digit one? Why does one appear more often in the pagination than nine?
2. How many sheets of paper would be required if the book were printed front to back?
3. What would the approximate weight of the book be? How would you find this weight?
4. How many odd numbers are there? What about even numbers?
5. What is the sum of all the page numbers?
6. How many of the pages have two or more identical digits?
7. How many times do three consecutive digits appear?
8. How many palindromes are there?
9. How many digits are there in 100 pages? ...200? ...300? Is there a pattern here?

Solutions

There would be 1049 pages in a book that is numbered consecutively starting with one and uses 3089 digits. This assumes that the pages are not numbered front to back. There are many possible methods for determining this answer. One is shown here.

1. Find the number of digits used on pages one to 100:
   one digit x nine numbers = 9
   two digits x 90 numbers = 180
   three digits x one number = 3
   Digits used: 192
2. Find the number of digits used on pages 101 to 1000:
   three digits x 899 numbers = 2697
   four digits x one number = 4
   Digits used: 2701
3. Find the total number of digits used on pages one to 1000:
   192 + 2701 = 2893
   Total digits: 2893
4. Find the number of additional digits needed:
   3089 – 2893 = 196
   Additional digits needed: 196
5. Find the number of additional pages needed:
   196 ÷ 4 = 49
   Additional pages needed: 49
6. Add the additional pages needed to the 1000 pages already used to get the total of **1049 pages**.

* Reprinted with permission from *Principles and Standards for School Mathematics*, 2000 by the National Council of Teachers of Mathematics. All rights reserved.

RAGES Over Pages

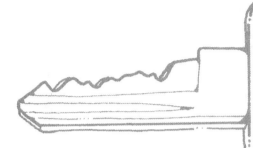

Key Question

How many pages are in a book numbered consecutively (starting with one) and requiring a total of 3089 digits to paginate?

Learning Goal

Students will:

determine the number of pages in a book numbered consecutively (starting with one) and requiring a total of 3089 digits to paginate.

How To Control
PAGE
RAGE!
by Haus Tility

RAGES Over Pages

Part One

The pages in a book are numbered consecutively starting with one. The page numbers contain a total of 3089 digits. How many pages are in the book? (The pages are not printed front to back.) Show how you found your answer in the space below.

How To Control
PAGE
RAGE!
by Haus Tility

Share your problem-solving approach with others in the class.

RAGES Over Pages

Part Two

Think of as many questions as you can that are related to the problem on the first page. List these questions below.

Pick one or two questions that you find especially interesting and work on them. Be prepared to share why you chose those questions and what you found out.

Connecting Learning

1. How many pages are there in the book? How do you know?

2. What methods did your group use to arrive at this answer? How do these methods compare to those used by other groups?

3. What extensions did you think of to explore?

4. What did you discover when you explored these extensions?

5. What problem-solving strategies did you use?

Practice Problems

The problems on the following pages are provided for additional practice with the problem-solving strategies covered in this book. No strategies have been recommended for the individual problems, and they do not follow any particular order. Students must decide which strategy to use based on the individual problem. It is suggested that the problems be copied onto transparencies and cut apart. A problem can then be placed on the overhead as a "bright beginning" to start math class or at any time during the day when a few minutes are available for review. To receive maximum benefit from the problems, be sure to have a time of discussion after each one where the emphasis is on the process and strategies used rather than arriving at the correct answer.

If you make a cube with 27 wooden blocks, what would be the cube's dimensions (in blocks)?

How many different coin combinations make 50 cents?

What is the largest number you can make using the seven digits in your phone number? ...the smallest?

Using pattern blocks, make a quilt square that is $\frac{1}{4}$ red.

If you link 20 paper clips, what is the largest area you can get if the shape can only have right angles?

The first four triangular numbers are 1, 3, 6, 10. What is the 7th number in this series?

What is the radius of the largest circle you can draw on a piece of notebook paper?

A man is 30 years older than his youngest son. In 17 years he will be twice his son's age. How old is the son now?

I'm thinking of a number. Multiply the number by two. Then add 11. The answer is 39. What is the number?

Can you find the values of X, Y, and Z to make this problem true?

$$\begin{array}{r} X\,Y\,Z \\ -\ Z\,Z \\ \hline X\,Y \end{array}$$

Place the digits 9, 7, 6, 5, 4, and 1 in the boxes in order to get the largest result.

☐☐ x ☐☐ + ☐ x ☐ =

On safari, you see eight ostriches and 11 giraffes. How many legs do you see?

At the zoo you see three cheetahs and five zebras. How many legs aren't striped?

Divide the face of the clock into three parts with two lines so that the sums of the numbers in the three parts are equal.

I'm thinking of a number. Three times the number plus 23 equals 53. What is the number?

There is a stairway made of cubes. How many cubes would be needed to make the steps nine steps high?

There are 60 seconds in one minute and 60 minutes in one hour. How many seconds are in one year? (not a leap year)

There are 8 people at a party. Everyone shakes hands with everyone else How many handshakes are there total?

If one candy bar is eight inches long, how many candy bars would be in a mile if they were laid end to end?

Ming got 78%, 62%, and 100% on her tests. What is her average score?

Four pennies laid side by side measure three inches in length. How many pennies would it take to cover a distance of two miles?

An egg crate came with 24 cracked eggs. That was $\frac{1}{6}$ of the total number of eggs. How many eggs were in the crate?

What number is in the 27th position of this pattern:

1, 4, 7, 10, 13... _____?

Complete these patterns:

3, 12, 48, 192, ____, ____, ____

1, 5, 25, 125, ____, ____, ____

Jordan has a new pony. She wants to build a rectangular pen in her yard. She wants the pen to be 65 feet long and 80 feet wide. How many feet of fencing does she need?

A movie sold 1572 tickets on the first day it was out. On its second day, it sold 1753 tickets. On its third day, it sold 152 less than on its second day. How many tickets were sold in three days?

A company makes 540 tons of cereal annually. Last year $1/9$ of the cereal was spoiled. How many tons of cereal were not spoiled?

We had a car wash. We charged $5 for cars and $10 for trucks. We washed 13 cars and two trucks. How much money did we earn?

Chin had $5.00 to spend on lunch. He bought a hamburger for $1.25, French fries for 65¢, and two drinks for 85¢ each. How much money did he get back?

Each week, you put $5.00 dollars in the bank for college. This is $1/10$ of your weekly allowance. What is your allowance?

A ball is dropped from a height of 100 meters. Each time it hits the ground, it bounces $1/2$ of the height it fell. How far will the ball have traveled when it hits the ground for the third time?

Find the one-digit number that when you multiply it by three, add eight, divide by two, and subtract six, you will get the number you started with.

987654321
Put addition signs into the number above so that you get a sum of 99. How many do you need? Where do they go?

There are 12 people in a room. Six people are wearing socks, four people are wearing shoes, and three people are wearing both. How many people are not wearing shoes or socks?

Mikayla and Aidan are playing a dice game. They need to know all the products they can get by rolling two dice. What products are possible?

I'm thinking of a number. Multiply the number by itself and then by itself again and you will get 216. What is the number?

Find answers for

$1 \times 8 + 1 =$ _____

$12 \times 8 + 2 =$ _____

$123 \times 8 + 3 =$ _____

$1234 \times 8 + 4 =$ _____

Predict the answer for

$123{,}456 \times 8 + 6 =$ _____

You have a penny, a nickel, a dime, and a quarter. What amounts can you make if you use one, two, three, or four of the coins?

Flip a coin 25 times and record the number of times it lands heads up and the number of times it lands tails up.

A man has to be at work by 9:00 AM. It takes him 15 minutes to get dressed, 20 minutes to eat, and 35 minutes to drive to work. What time should he get up?

A crab is walking along the beach. It goes three steps left, one step right, two steps left, and then eight steps left. What will the crab have to do to get back where it started?

On the quiz show "Who Knows What?" each question is worth four times as much as the previous question. The fourth question is worth $1600. How much is the first question worth?

Markisa and Chris were playing a factors game. Markisa would name a factor of 48 and Chris would give the other factor. Make a table to show the different factors of 48 that Markisa and Chris could have used.

Jerome saw the results of a survey showing ice cream preferences. There were 10 people surveyed. Eight people liked vanilla and six people liked chocolate. How many people liked both?

We are having a party and are putting square tables together in a long row for the party. We can put three chairs on each side of a table. The tables are all the same size. If we put together 12 tables in a row, how many people can we seat?

Allen saw all sorts of comic books divided into three piles. One pile was marked 10¢, the second 5¢, and the third 1¢. He had 26¢. How many different combinations of comic books could Allen buy?

Fred began a weight-training program. The first week, he lifted 12 pounds. For the next three weeks, he lifted 13, 14.5, and 16.5 pounds. If he continues this pattern, during which week will he lift more than 50 pounds?

There are five people waiting in line. Each person is wearing a different color shirt. The person wearing brown is at the front of the line. The person in yellow is right before the person in red. The person in blue is not last. The person in green is right behind the person in red. In what order are the people standing?

Daniel arranged loaves of bread on six shelves in the bakery. He put one loaf on the top shelf, three loaves on the second shelf, and five loaves on the third shelf. If he continues this pattern, how many loaves will Daniel put on the sixth shelf?

Billy noticed that his dog was eating more every day. The first day, his dog ate five treats. The second day, his dog had 11. The third day he had 18 treats. The fourth day he had 26 treats. On what day did Billy's dog eat 56 treats?

There are cans and bottles of soda at the store. Two cans and one bottle of soda weigh the same as five cans of soda. If a can of soda weighs 12 ounces, then what does a bottle of soda weigh?

During the day, Joe spent $8.00 on breakfast, withdrew $40.00 from the ATM, got his dry cleaning for $12.00, bought five shirts for $22.00 each. At the end of the day, he had $100.00. How much did he start the day with?

It took Juan one hour 25 minutes to walk from home to the start of the Meadow Trail. Then it took 25 minutes to walk to the meadow at the end. He arrived at the meadow at 2:45 PM. At what time did he leave home?

Bob, Miguel, and Jacob left the theater together. Each one was wearing the jacket and the shoes of someone else. Miguel was wearing Jacob's jacket and Bob's shoes. Whose jacket and whose shoes were Jacob and Bob wearing?

I have a piece of string that is 40 centimeters long. It is cut into three pieces. The longest piece is three times as long as the middle-sized piece and the shortest piece is 23 centimeters shorter than the longest piece. Find the lengths of the three pieces.

Olivia, Muhammad, Ethan, and Tiffany shared a pizza for lunch. Olivia, had $3/8$ of the pizza, Muhammad had $1/4$ of the pizza and Ethan had $1/8$ of the pizza. How much pizza was left over for Tiffany?

A painting of the circus shows two overlapping rings. In the rings are elephants. There are 11 elephants in the left ring and nine elephants in the right ring. Five of the elephants are in both rings. How many elephants are there total?

The kitchen servants brought in four pies left over from the feast. Twelve pies were eaten at the feast. Queen Mabel took two pies home. How many pies did the servants bring into the feast at the beginning?

James began writing a book. At the end of the first week, he had written 10 pages. By the end of the second week, he had written six more pages, for a total of 16 pages. At the end of the third week, he had a total of 23 pages and by the end of the fourth week he had 31 pages completed in his book. If he continues writing at this same rate, how many pages will his book have at the end of the seventh week?

Mary and her friends began an exercise group. They decided to walk along a trail each day. On the first day, they walked $^2/_3$ of the trail. On the second day, they walked $^3/_5$ of the trail. On the third day, they walked $^4/_7$, and on the fourth day they walked $^5/_9$. If this pattern continues, how far will Mary and her friends walk on the tenth day?

Gardener Lee wants to plant grass seed in his front yard. Grass seed is available in three-pound boxes and in five-pound boxes. A three-pound box costs $4.50, and a five-pound box costs $5.60. Gardener Lee needs 17 pounds of the grass seed. How many of each size box should he purchase? How much will it cost?

What is the number?
- There is a one in the thousands place.
- The digit in the tens place is nine times the digit in the thousands place.
- The digit in the ones place is three less than the number in the hundreds place.
- The digit in the hundreds is two less than the number in the tens place.

You went to a water park with a friend. You spent half of your money on admission to the park. You forgot to bring a towel, so you spent half the money that was left on a new one. Then you had $4 left, which you spent on lunch. How much money did you start with?

Tamara gave half of her money to Allison. Then she gave 1/4 of what she had left to Lauren. Tamara then saw David, and she gave him 1/3 of what she had left. Now Tamara equally shares the money she has left with you. You get $2. How much money did Tamara have to start with?

The AIMS Program

AIMS is the acronym for "Activities Integrating Mathematics and Science." Such integration enriches learning and makes it meaningful and holistic. AIMS began as a project of Fresno Pacific University to integrate the study of mathematics and science in grades K-9, but has since expanded to include language arts, social studies, and other disciplines.

AIMS is a continuing program of the non-profit AIMS Education Foundation. It had its inception in a National Science Foundation funded program whose purpose was to explore the effectiveness of integrating mathematics and science. The project directors in cooperation with 80 elementary classroom teachers devoted two years to a thorough field-testing of the results and implications of integration.

The approach met with such positive results that the decision was made to launch a program to create instructional materials incorporating this concept. Despite the fact that thoughtful educators have long recommended an integrative approach, very little appropriate material was available in 1981 when the project began. A series of writing projects have ensued, and today the AIMS Education Foundation is committed to continue the creation of new integrated activities on a permanent basis.

The AIMS program is funded through the sale of books, products, and staff development workshops and through proceeds from the Foundation's endowment. All net income from program and products flows into a trust fund administered by the AIMS Education Foundation. Use of these funds is restricted to support of research, development, and publication of new materials. Writers donate all their rights to the Foundation to support its on-going program. No royalties are paid to the writers.

The rationale for integration lies in the fact that science, mathematics, language arts, social studies, etc., are integrally interwoven in the real world from which it follows that they should be similarly treated in the classroom where we are preparing students to live in that world. Teachers who use the AIMS program give enthusiastic endorsement to the effectiveness of this approach.

Science encompasses the art of questioning, investigating, hypothesizing, discovering, and communicating. Mathematics is the language that provides clarity, objectivity, and understanding. The language arts provide us powerful tools of communication. Many of the major contemporary societal issues stem from advancements in science and must be studied in the context of the social sciences. Therefore, it is timely that all of us take seriously a more holistic mode of educating our students. This goal motivates all who are associated with the AIMS Program. We invite you to join us in this effort.

Meaningful integration of knowledge is a major recommendation coming from the nation's professional science and mathematics associations. The American Association for the Advancement of Science in *Science for All Americans* strongly recommends the integration of mathematics, science, and technology. The National Council of Teachers of Mathematics places strong emphasis on applications of mathematics such as are found in science investigations. AIMS is fully aligned with these recommendations.

Extensive field testing of AIMS investigations confirms these beneficial results:

1. Mathematics becomes more meaningful, hence more useful, when it is applied to situations that interest students.
2. The extent to which science is studied and understood is increased, with a significant economy of time, when mathematics and science are integrated.
3. There is improved quality of learning and retention, supporting the thesis that learning that is meaningful and relevant is more effective.
4. Motivation and involvement are increased dramatically as students investigate real-world situations and participate actively in the process.

We invite you to become part of this classroom teacher movement by using an integrated approach to learning and sharing any suggestions you may have. The AIMS Program welcomes you!

AIMS Education Foundation Programs

Practical proven strategies to improve student achievement

When you host an AIMS workshop for elementary and middle school educators, you will know your teachers are receiving effective usable training they can apply in their classrooms immediately.

Designed for teachers—AIMS Workshops:

* Correlate to your state standards;
* Address key topic areas, including math content, science content, problem solving, and process skills;
* Teach you how to use AIMS' effective hands-on approach;
* Provide practice of activity-based teaching;
* Address classroom management issues, higher-order thinking skills, and materials;
* Give you AIMS resources; and
* Offer college (graduate-level) credits for many courses.

Aligned to district and administrator needs—AIMS workshops offer:

* Flexible scheduling and grade span options;
* Custom (one-, two-, or three-day) workshops to meet specific schedule, topic and grade-span needs;
* Pre-packaged one-day workshops on most major topics—only $3900 for up to 30 participants (includes all materials and expenses);
* Prepackaged four- or five-day workshops for in-depth math and science training—only $12,300 for up to 30 participants (includes all materials and expenses);
* Sustained staff development, by scheduling work-shops throughout the school year and including follow-up and assessment;
* Eligibility for funding under the Title I and Title II sections of No Child Left Behind; and

* Affordable professional development—save when you schedule consecutive-day workshops.

University Credit—Correspondence Courses

AIMS offers correspondence courses through a partnership with Fresno Pacific University.

* Convenient distance-learning courses—you study at your own pace and schedule. No computer or Internet access required!

The tuition for each three-semester unit graduate-level course is $264 plus a materials fee.

The AIMS Instructional Leadership Program

This is an AIMS staff-development program seeking to prepare facilitators for leadership roles in science/math education in their home districts or regions. Upon successful completion of the program, trained facilitators become members of the AIMS Instructional Leadership Network, qualified to conduct AIMS workshops, teach AIMS in-service courses for college credit, and serve as AIMS consultants. Intensive training is provided in mathematics, science, process and thinking skills, workshop management, and other relevant topics.

Introducing AIMS Science Core Curriculum

Developed to meet 100% of your state's standards, AIMS' Science Core Curriculum gives students the opportunity to build content knowledge, thinking skills, and fundamental science processes.

* *Each* grade specific module has been developed to extend the AIMS approach to full-year science programs.
* *Each* standards-based module includes math, reading, hands-on investigations, and assessments.

Like all AIMS resources, these core modules are able to serve students at all stages of readiness, making these a great value across the grades served in your school.

For current information regarding the programs described above, please complete the following form and mail it to: P.O. Box 8120, Fresno, CA 93747.

Information Request

Please send current information on the items checked:

____ *Basic Information Packet* on AIMS materials ____ Hosting information for AIMS workshops
____ *AIMS Instructional Leadership Program* ____ AIMS Science Core Curriculum

Name _____ Phone _____

Address_____
  Street   City   State   Zip

Magazine

**YOUR K-9 MATH AND SCIENCE
CLASSROOM ACTIVITIES RESOURCE**

The AIMS Magazine is your source for standards-based, hands-on math and science investigations. Each issue is filled with teacher-friendly, ready-to-use activities that engage students in meaningful learning.

- *Four issues each year (fall, winter, spring, and summer).*

Current issue is shipped with all past issues within that volume.

1820	Volume	XX	2005-2006	$19.95
1821	Volume	XXI	2006-2007	$19.95
1822	Volume	XXII	2007-2008	$19.95

Two-Volume Combination

M20507	Volumes XX & XXI	2005-2007	$34.95
M20608	Volumes XXI & XXII	2006-2008	$34.95

Back Volumes Available
Complete volumes available for purchase:

1802	Volume II	1987-1988	$19.95
1804	Volume IV	1989-1990	$19.95
1805	Volume V	1990-1991	$19.95
1807	Volume VII	1992-1993	$19.95
1808	Volume VIII	1993-1994	$19.95
1809	Volume IX	1994-1995	$19.95
1810	Volume X	1995-1996	$19.95
1811	Volume XI	1996-1997	$19.95
1812	Volume XII	1997-1998	$19.95
1813	Volume XIII	1998-1999	$19.95
1814	Volume XIV	1999-2000	$19.95
1815	Volume XV	2000-2001	$19.95
1816	Volume XVI	2001-2002	$19.95
1817	Volume XVII	2002-2003	$19.95
1818	Volume XVIII	2003-2004	$19.95
1819	Volume XIX	2004-2005	$35.00

Volumes II to XIX include 10 issues.

Call 1.888.733.2467 or go to www.aimsedu.org

Subscribe to the AIMS Magazine

$19.95 a year!

AIMS Magazine is published four times a year.

Subscriptions ordered at any time will receive all the issues for that year.

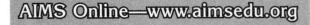

AIMS Online—www.aimsedu.org

To see all that AIMS has to offer, check us out on the Internet at www.aimsedu.org. At our website you can search our activities database; preview and purchase individual AIMS activities; learn about core curriculum, college courses, and workshops; buy manipulatives and other classroom resources; and download free resources including articles, puzzles, and sample AIMS activities.

AIMS News
While visiting the AIMS website, sign up for AIMS News, our FREE e-mail newsletter. You'll get the latest information on what's new at AIMS including:

- New publications;
- New core curriculum modules; and
- New materials.

Sign up today!